Chapter 1
Introducing Wine

Fundamental facts

What is wine?

Wine has been defined by the European Community as follows:

"Wine is the product obtained from the total or partial alcoholic fermentation of fresh grapes, whether or not crushed, or of grape must."

The process of converting juice into wine is dealt with in Chapter 4.

How much is produced?

World production of wine in 1988 amounted to more than thirty thousand million litres. Consumption tends to be concentrated in those regions where wine is produced.

Where is wine produced?

Two-thirds of the world's wine is produced in western and eastern Europe, with Italy, France, the Soviet Union and Spain being the major contributors in terms of quantity. In respect of the UK market, the wines of Germany, Portugal and Bulgaria are also significant. In the remaining parts of the world, leading producers are Argentina, Chile, USA, South Africa and Australia.

Each of these countries has a suitable climate for wine grape production. The importance of climate is dealt with in Chapter 4.

Most wine producing countries make several different types of wine.

Wine Types

Light wine

The simplest type of wine, made all over the world. The sugar in the grape is converted into alcohol, normally between 8% and 15% vol. (between 8 and 15 parts of alcohol per 100 of liquid by volume). Light wines often complement the food of their region. They are discussed in Chapters 5, 6 and 7.

Liqueur wine

The level of alcohol is increased by adding brandy or other types of grape spirit. Examples of liqueur wine include **port** and **sherry**. They are often referred to as **fortified wines**. + madeira

Sparkling wine

Carbon dioxide gas is trapped in the wine before the bottle is sealed. When the bottle is opened and the wine drunk, bubbles of gas are released. There are several methods of making sparkling wine and they are described in Chapter 8. The most famous example is made in Champagne, in northern France.

Aromatised wine

The wine is flavoured with herbs or spices, and is usually also a liqueur wine. The wine of this type most often drunk in the UK is **vermouth**. Aromatised wines and liqueur wines are dealt with in Chapter 9.

Wine Styles

Each type of wine may be made in a variety of styles, according to:

colour	red, white or pink (rosé)
sweetness	dry, medium or sweet.

Methods of production are discussed in Chapter 4.

Chapter 2
Handling Wine

Storage of Wines

Some wines are mature when still young and are ready for drinking soon after they have been bottled, for example, beaujolais nouveau and muscadet.

Other wines, such as vintage port and top quality red bordeaux wines, take many years to reach maturity. In either case correct storage is very important.

If wine is kept in poor conditions, it will deteriorate and become undrinkable early in its life.

Storage in a Cellar

The ideal cellar conditions for the storage of wine are:

(a) The temperature should be constant and cool. The ideal temperature is 13 degrees Celcius (13°C), but slight variation on either side is acceptable, between 10 and 15°C. Too much heat will encourage the wine to deteriorate.

(b) The storage area should not be exposed to strong light. Light can age a wine prematurely as well as causing the labels to fade.

(c) The area should be clean and dry. Damp conditions can cause deterioration of cartons and labels. They also encourage cork weevils, which can destroy the cork.

(d) The storage area should be free from any vibration which would disturb the wine.

(e) Bottles should be kept lying on their sides, with the label uppermost. In this way corks are kept moist by contact with the wine. If a cork dries out it will shrink. Air and bacteria can then enter and spoil the wine. Any deposit in maturing wines such as vintage port or claret will form on the opposite side to the label, making it easier to see when decanting. (see page 5).

Liqueur wines (apart from vintage port) and spirits (whisky, gin, brandy, etc) should be stored upright.

Storage in a Shop

Spirits and liqueur wines may be kept on the higher shelves (hot air rises). White light wines should be stored on the lowest shelves, and red wines above them.

Wines displayed in the shop window are liable to an excess of light and strong temperature variations. Therefore a strict stock rotation should be used to prevent spoilage - ideally all bottles in the window should be replaced each week.

Service of Wines

When serving wine in a restaurant, the unopened bottle should be presented to the host for approval. This ensures that the wine is the same as was ordered.

Opening Still Wines

1. **Remove the top of the capsule**, by cutting round below the lip of the bottle. This can be done either with a capsule remover or with a sharp knife.

2. **Clean the neck** of the bottle with a clean cloth.

3. **Draw the cork**. There are many types of corkscrew available today, the most popular varieties as illustrated here. The important thing is to draw the cork as gently and cleanly as possible.

From left: waiter's friend, screwpull and butterfly corkscrews

4. **Give the neck of the bottle a final clean,** inside and outside.

5. **Pour a sample into the host's glass for approval.** When this has been given, fill the glasses of the other guests. Never fill the glasses more than two-thirds full, as this inhibits the full appreciation of all the characteristics of the wine.

Decanting

Some wines with a heavy deposit need to be decanted. This deposit is quite natural and is formed during the ageing process of many good red wines.

First remove the bottle horizontally from its rack and place in a decanting basket.

Then remove the top of the capsule and clean the shoulder and neck of the bottle.

Very gently remove the cork and wipe inside the rim to clean it.

Finally, remove the bottle from the basket, being careful not to disturb the deposit. Holding the bottle in front of a light, pour the wine carefully into the decanter until the deposit can be seen near the neck. At this point stop pouring.

Opening Sparkling Wines

It is important to remember that there is very considerable pressure in a bottle of sparkling wine. Chilling to the correct temperature helps to reduce this pressure. Even when the wine is chilled, it is possible for the cork to spring violently from the bottle and injure someone.

First remove the foil and then the wire muzzle. The cork must be held in place by the hand from the moment the wire is removed.

Tilt the bottle at an angle of about 30 degrees, gripping the cork, and use the other hand to grip the base of the bottle. Turn the bottle, not the cork. Hold the cork steady, resisting its tendency to fly out, and ease it slowly out of the bottle.

The gas pressure should be released with a quiet "phut". Explosions and flying corks, as seen so frequently at sports meetings, are quite incorrect and wasteful.

Should the cork stick, pincers may be used to ease the cork out.

Temperatures for Serving Wine

(a)   **Light-bodied white wines**

These should be served cool, but not too cold as this inhibits the aromas and flavours of the wine. Cellar temperature between 10 and 15°C, is perfect.

(b)   **Full-bodied white wines, sweet white wines and sparkling wines**

These are also served chilled, but may be colder than lighter styles.

White and rosé wines are customarily served in an ice bucket. This should not be filled with ice, but should be of cold water with some ice in it.

(c)   **Red wines**

Red wines should be served at room temperature, anywhere between 15 and 20°C.

The term **room temperature** refers to a comfortable but cool living room: if red wine is over-warmed, it alters its character and can even taste slightly burnt.

Full-bodied red wines should be uncorked up to two hours before serving and lighter ones up to one hour.

If the red wine is very old, then open the wine just before serving it.

Some especially light red wines can benefit from slight chilling. Such wines include some beaujolais and valpolicella.

Glasses

There are many differently shaped glasses available, some of which are designed for individual types of wine. One of the most commonly used is the paris goblet. It has a broad base and narrower top to increase the bouquet, and is suitable for all light wines.

Sparkling wines should be served in the flute glass as illustrated below. This shape enhances the effect of the bubbles. Conversely, in the flat saucer-shaped glass the bubbles are lost and the aroma cannot be fully appreciated.

Paris goblet

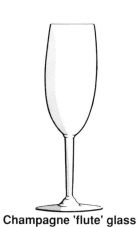

Champagne 'flute' glass

The Responsible Appreciation of Alcohol

The drinks industry places increasing emphasis on the responsible appreciation of alcoholic beverages.

Responsibility begins with observance of the laws prohibiting the sale of alcohol to young people. In the UK the minimum age for purchasing an alcoholic beverage is 18.

Dangers exist in two principal ways. Mild intoxication can impair a person's ability to perform potentially dangerous tasks, such as driving a motor vehicle or operating factory machinery.

Regular excessive drinking can lead to permanent ill-health, as well as behavioural, emotional and economic problems.

Assessing Intake of Alcohol

In order to guard against these problems, consumers need to assess reliably how much alcohol they have taken . There is a simple relationship between different drinks in terms of the amount of alcohol they contain. In standard measures, each type of drink contains a similar amount of alcohol, known as one **unit.**

> One unit = a half pint of ordinary beer or lager (at 3.5% vol)
> or
> a single measure of spirits (whisky, gin, brandy, etc) (at 40% vol)
> or
> a glass of wine
> or
> a small glass of sherry
> or
> a measure of vermouth

On average, the effects of alcohol wear off at the rate of one unit per hour.

The law is concerned with the alcohol level in the blood, measured in milligrammes per 100 millilitres (mg/100ml).

Drinking and Driving

The fact that it is dangerous to drive with alcohol in the bloodstream, is reinforced by legislation in many countries.

In 1989 the UK legal limit of 80mg/100ml was shared by many countries, both inside and outside Europe. The amount of alcohol needed to reach this limit varies between individuals, but for some it can be as low as three units.

The Danger to Health

The accumulative effects of regular alcoholic consumption are difficult to chart precisely. Few would dispute however, the strong correlation between excessive drinking and the onset of liver cirrhosis.

The Health Education Authority has advised that damage to health is almost unknown in:

(a)   men who consume no more than 21 units per week, or

(b)   women who consume no more than 14 units per week.

Chapter 3
Tasting and Evaluating Wine

Educated tasting is a combination of knowledge, experience and learning the disciplined use of the three senses involved:

sight • **smell** • **taste**

As knowledge improves and practice grows, the taster becomes more skilful, which enhances the enjoyment and understanding of wine.

Reasons for Tasting and Writing Notes

There are four related reasons:

(a)   to provide a personal record of wines tasted;

(b)   to assist in the description of a wine when explaining its qualities or deficiencies to other people;

(c)   to help in the assessment of the quality of a wine in terms of value - eg: when making a purchasing decision;

(d)   to monitor the progress of a wine, an essential part of protecting investment.

Tasting Conditions

Professional tasting should always be done in neutral conditions.

Perfect surroundings are :

       good daylight
       north facing windows
       clean white surfaces
       no distracting odours

A professional tasting room

The requirement for no distracting odours, is very important. Aromas from perfume or aftershave affect the bouquet of the wine and make it impossible for other people to taste properly. Fumes of any kind and kitchen smells should be avoided.

Glasses

These should be completely clean, dry and polished. They should be washed in hot water only, without detergent which leaves a distinct odour.

Glasses should be broader at the base and narrower at the top. This helps concentrate the aroma towards the nose.

Suitable shapes for tasting are:

> Paris goblet
> Sherry copita
> ISO (International Standards Organisation) tasting glass

The tasting process

In order to taste accurately, only a small amount should be poured into the tasting glass. Filling it more than one-third full makes it difficult to perform some of the following operations.

All wines have certain characteristics in common. These are:

Sweetness/dryness
Acidity
Tannin
Weight or body
Fruit

ISO glass, illustrating the correct filling level

In tasting, sight, smell and taste are used to recognise these factors. They also help to judge the health and quality of the wine.

Sight

Look for the following points:-

Clarity   Is the wine bright and healthy looking or is it hazy or cloudy?

Intensity   Is the colour deep or pale?

Colour   Hold the glass at an angle against a white background and assess the colour, especially at the edge or rim.

Red wines begin life as purple, changing with age to red, mahogany and, eventually, brown.

The change in colour is best seen on the rim of the wine, as shown above.

Smell

The smell of a wine is known as its 'nose'.

While assessing the nose, the various aromas may be released by swirling the wine in the glass. This also allows the oxygen from the air to freshen the wine and bring it into peak condition.

Sniff gently, but deeply, and look for the following:-

Condition   Does the wine smell pleasant and clean, or is there any mustiness, earthiness, or smell of bad eggs?

Intensity   Is the nose weak or pronounced?

Character

The actual description of the fruit character is difficult at first. Constant practice will highlight various fruit or flower characteristics.

Examples include grape, blackcurrant, raspberry, soft fruits, flowery, violets, lychees, apples, peaches, apricots, honey, nuts, petrol, oak, vanilla, spice, bread, yeast, smoke - and many others.

Taste

The taste of the wine, which is called the 'palate', reveals the true nature of the wine.

Take a small mouthful and swirl it around the mouth, so that it contacts all parts of the mouth, tongue, gums, soft palate. This is necessary because different parts of the mouth are sensitive to different tastes.

Additionally, and this is what makes tasters at work look so odd, lean the face forward so that the wine rests on the teeth, purse the lips and suck air in through the mouth. This needs a little practice, but is well worth it, as the flavours in the wine are really drawn out.

It is now possible to assess the following:

Sweetness Sweetness is immediately noticeable on the front of the tongue. A wine with no sugar is called 'dry'.

Acidity Lemon juice is acidic and makes the mouth water. This is quite different from the effect of tannin. Acidity is very important in wine, as it gives the wine 'balance'. Too much and the wine is tart, too little and the wine is flabby.

Tannin This is the substance that makes young red wines seem harsh. It is felt on teeth, gums and tongue and makes the mouth feel dry. As red wines mature, the tannin comes out of the wine, forming part of the deposit. The wine then tastes more balanced. To experience the taste of tannin, just brew a cup of very strong tea!

Weight   This is the general 'feel' of the wine in the mouth. German wines feel light, southern wines like Chateauneuf-du-Pape feel big and heavy.

Fruit   The overall taste of fruit in the mouth. In general, the better the wine, the greater the level of fruit.

Length   This strange term simply means how long the flavour lingers after spitting (or swallowing!). Usually the longer the better.

Conclusions

Finally, after tasting, it is necessary to evaluate the wine.

The main points to decide are:

Quality   Quality is a judgement of whether the wine is a good example of its kind, or merely an ordinary one.

Maturity   This is a measure of the state of readiness for drinking. Age and maturity are not the same. Many wines are made to drink at less than a year old, whereas other wines still taste young when ten years old.

Chapter 4
Producing Wine

Wine is an alcoholic beverage made from the juice of freshly picked grapes.

This definition does not explain why two wines can be so different from one another. Consider for example a mellow liebfraumilch and a steely, dry chablis, or a firm, red bordeaux and a light, fresh bardolino.

Many styles of wine are produced, which suit people's various preferences. There are six factors which affect the final taste and style of the wine.

Climate
Soil
Grape variety
Viticulture (method of growing the vine)
Vinification (method of turning grapes into wine)
Annual weather conditions

Climate

The shaded areas on the map on the following page, show the main wine producing regions of the world. All of these regions lie between latitudes 30 and 50 degrees north and south of the equator. Within these zones the grapes will ripen satisfactorily to make a good wine.

There is a wide range of climates. For example, in the cool, damp conditions of England and Germany, it is sometimes difficult for the grapes to ripen fully. At the other extreme, in the hot, dry North African countries such as Morocco and Algeria, the problems are too much heat and insufficient rain, leading to overripe grapes with low acidity.

The local geography will also affect the climate surrounding a vineyard. For example in the northern hemisphere, vineyards planted on south-facing slopes will be warmer, because of increased exposure to the sun.

The proximity of water can increase humidity and moderate changes in temperature.

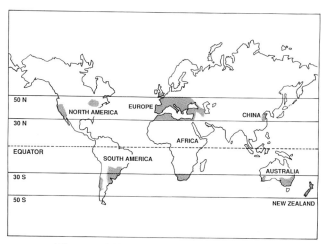

The world's wine producing regions

The Ideal Climate

If an ideal climate were ever to exist it would include sufficient moisture and warmth to enable the vines to grow and the grapes to ripen. Furthermore, the right weather conditions must prevail during the various stages of the growth cycle of the vines.

Perfect conditions would be:

A cold winter to inhibit growth and rest the vine. Frosts to kill diseases, but not so severe as to kill the vine. Enough rain to build moisture reserves in the soil.

A mild, warm spring with gentle rain to encourage the vine's growth.

A warm settled period during the vine's flowering, followed by a hot summer with a little rain to swell the developing fruit.

A long, fine, dry autumn to complete the ripening of the grape, and for the vintage.

Main Climatic Dangers

FROST, which can destroy growing shoots in the spring and is particularly dangerous at the time of budding.

HAIL, which can break and damage young growth and, especially during late summer, burst developing grapes allowing rot to set in.

WIND, which is disastrous at flowering, preventing pollination. It can also break young shoots.

Soil

The grape vine often thrives where other plants fail. Generally speaking:

poor soil - low yields of fine quality wine
rich soil - higher yields of less good quality wine

Vines planted in poor soils are forced to grow a deep and extensive root system to extract moisture and nutrients from the subsoil, which is rich in minerals.

These minerals, which include copper, iron and magnesium, enrich the juice of the grape and intensify the flavour of the wine.

Throughout the wine producing latitudes, there are many different soil types.

Chalky or limestone-rich soils are frequently used for the production of good white wines, for example in Champagne, Burgundy or Jerez (sherry).

The chalky 'albariza' soil of Jerez helps the production of grapes for the best sherry.

Granite soils, on the other hand, are more suited to the production of red wines, as typified by the Beaujolais district in southern Burgundy.

Gamay vines in the granite-rich soil of Beaujolais

Whatever the soil, good drainage is essential

The best soils provide good drainage *naturally*.

Grape Varieties

Most vines producing grapes suitable for making wine belong to the species ***vitis vinifera***.

There are some 3,000 varieties of *vitis vinifera* suitable for wine, and in the classic European areas, the vines planted are usually determined by the soil and the climate, and have become traditional over many generations.

A small number of varieties have established a reputation over many years for making outstanding wine.

These are known as **noble grapes**. They often produce good wine when planted in new areas.

Examples of such 'noble grapes' and their traditional regions are:-

White: Riesling - Rheingau/Alsace   Chardonnay - Burgundy

Red: Cabernet Sauvignon - Bordeaux   Pinot Noir - Burgundy

The Use of American Rootstocks

During the second half of the last century, wholesale replanting of vineyards became necessary.

Between 1860 and 1900 the European *vitis vinifera* vines were devastated by a vine louse, known as *phylloxera vastatrix,* brought to Europe from the USA on imported vines. These burrowed through the soil and punctured the roots of the vine. This weakened and slowly killed the plant.

The louse began its progress in the south of France and in the following decades spread through Europe's vine growing areas.

The dreaded *phylloxera*, here depicted on a German wine cask

However, the vines grown on the east coast of America were found to be resistant to the ravages of this pest. These vines were in fact NOT examples of *vitis vinifera*, but of a few related species. The main examples are:

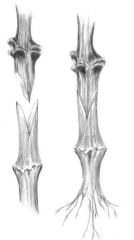

vitis rupestris
vitis riparia
vitis berlandieri

These vines produce wines with a flavour which is different from those produced from *vitis vinifera*, and therefore it was not felt possible to introduce them into the vineyards in place of *vitis vinifera* varieties. The remedy was to graft the shoots of *vitis vinifera* on to American vine rootstocks. This was first done in 1884.

The 'V' graft: a common form of grafting

Most new vines planted today consist of the shoot of a *vitis vinifera* (European) variety which has been grafted on to an American root.

19

Viticulture

The vineyard cycle

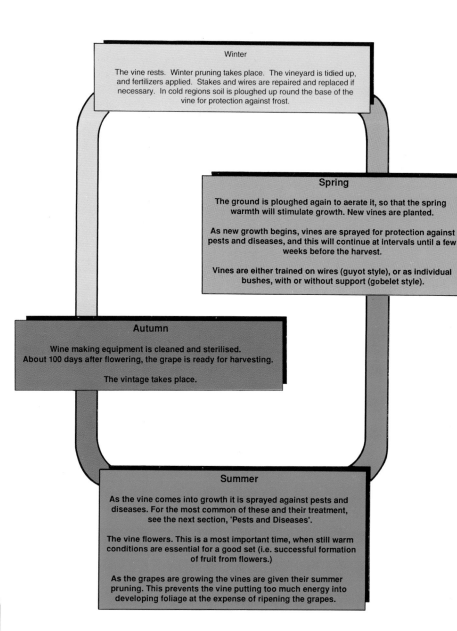

Winter

The vine rests. Winter pruning takes place. The vineyard is tidied up, and fertilizers applied. Stakes and wires are repaired and replaced if necessary. In cold regions soil is ploughed up round the base of the vine for protection against frost.

Spring

The ground is ploughed again to aerate it, so that the spring warmth will stimulate growth. New vines are planted.

As new growth begins, vines are sprayed for protection against pests and diseases, and this will continue at intervals until a few weeks before the harvest.

Vines are either trained on wires (guyot style), or as individual bushes, with or without support (gobelet style).

Autumn

Wine making equipment is cleaned and sterilised.
About 100 days after flowering, the grape is ready for harvesting.

The vintage takes place.

Summer

As the vine comes into growth it is sprayed against pests and diseases. For the most common of these and their treatment, see the next section, 'Pests and Diseases'.

The vine flowers. This is a most important time, when still warm conditions are essential for a good set (i.e. successful formation of fruit from flowers.)

As the grapes are growing the vines are given their summer pruning. This prevents the vine putting too much energy into developing foliage at the expense of ripening the grapes.

20

Pests and Diseases

Like every plant, the vine is subject to certain pests and diseases. The diseases usually attack the vine during the growing season and, as prevention is always better than cure, most vineyards begin spraying the vine as soon as growth starts.

Pests. The most serious pest is *phylloxera*. The remedy is to graft *vitis vinifera* vines on to resistant American rootstock.

Other common enemies of the vine include deer, rabbits, birds, grape berry moths, red spiders, wasps and weeds.

Diseases. The most serious diseases are:-

1. Powdery Mildew

Mildew

This fungus reached Europe from North America in 1850. It leaves a white deposit on new growth and on developing grapes which split and shrivel.

It is combatted by spraying with sulphur at flowering time. After flowering, the vines are dusted with sulphur powder.

2. Downy Mildew

A fungus which first appeared in Europe in 1878 and thrives in damp, humid conditions. The first signs are oily, transparent patches on the leaves, and if not treated, the fungus will destroy the grapes.

To prevent *peronospera*, vineyards are sprayed with Bordeaux mixture (copper sulphate, lime and water), or with other copper or zinc based sprays.

3. Grey Rot (*Pourriture grise*)

A fungus called *botrytis cinerea* attacks the vine in humid conditions, covering leaves and grapes with a grey mould. It destroys colour pigments in red grapes and gives an unpleasant taste to the wine from both red and white grapes. It is controlled by using anti-rot sprays.

Noble Rot

Noble rot shown here in a bunch of Gewürztraminer grapes in Germany

When humid conditions in the morning are followed by heat during the rest of the day, the same fungus, *botrytis cinerea*, can appear in its beneficial form, **noble rot** or *pourriture noble*. In this form it results in shrivelled grapes with very high sugar levels. Certain white grapes with thin skins are particularly susceptible to noble rot and these include semillon and riesling. The great sweet wines, such as sauternes and Trockenbeerenauslese, are made from grapes attacked by noble rot. (See sections on Bordeaux and Germany).

Having survived all the hazards of the vineyard, the grapes will complete their ripening in the autumn. This point is reached normally a hundred days after the flowering of the vine.

The picking of the grapes is known as THE VINTAGE.

Grapes are traditionally picked by hand, but today in areas of large, relatively flat vineyards, grapes are often harvested by machine.

Hand-picking in Burgundy

Machine-picking is possible if there are no steep gradients.

The essential part of vinification (the conversion of grape juice into wine) is FERMENTATION.

Man has been making wine for at least ten thousand years. Only since the middle of the last century has the biological process of fermentation been understood.

One of the great French scientists of the 19th century was Louis Pasteur, whose pioneering research in biochemistry contributed so much to natural science.

What is less well known is that Pasteur, after years of investigation, was the first person to understand the following fact:

Fermentation occurs when yeast feeds on sugars, converting them to alcohol and carbon dioxide gas (CO_2).

Yeast + Sugar = Alcohol + Carbon Dioxide

The diagram below shows the ingredients of a ripe grape.

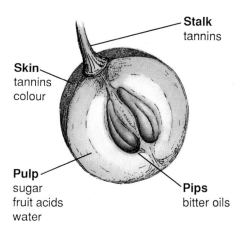

On the skin of the ripe grape is a dull, whitish-coloured film of waxy substance. This is known as the **bloom**. Yeasts and bacteria present in the air attach themselves to the bloom. On each grape there are millions of **wild yeasts** and thousands of **wine yeasts**. When the skin of the grape is broken the yeasts come into contact with the sugar in the pulp and fermentation can begin.

Fermentation may be NATURAL or CONTROLLED.

In **natural fermentation** the wild yeasts feed on the sugar and produce up to 4% of alcohol, but often also give a slightly unpleasant taste.

At this level of alcohol, the wild yeasts die and wine yeasts continue to work until....

there is no more sugar left to feed them

or

they are killed once the wine has reached a strength of about 15% alcohol.

After some time, the wine is spoilt by the action of bacteria, usually turning the wine into vinegar.

Natural fermentation was the original way of making wine. However, after Pasteur's discovery of the role of yeasts, methods of controlling fermentation were gradually developed.

Today wine is made by **controlled fermentation**.

There are two types of control which are applied:

1. The wild yeasts and bacteria are killed, allowing only the wine yeasts to work. This is done by adding a little sulphur dioxide (SO_2) to the grape juice before the start of fermentation. Levels of SO_2 are strictly controlled by the European Community (EC) wine regulations.

2. The temperature of fermentation is strictly controlled. Yeasts only work between 5°C and 35°C. The temperature must, therefore, be kept within these limits otherwise fermentation would come to a premature halt.

In general, white wines are fermented between 15°C and 20°C. Fermentation is slower at this temperature, so helping to preserve the aroma and flavour of the grapes.

Red wines are fermented at a higher temperature, 25°C to 30°C, which helps to extract colour from the skins.

Chaptalisation

Yeast feeding on sugar produces alcohol. It therefore follows that the final degree of alcohol created results from the amount of sugar present in the grapes.

In cool, difficult climatic conditions, such as in Germany, there may be some years when there is too little sun to ripen the grapes fully.

Increasing the alcohol helps to preserve the wine and balance its flavour.

Sugar may be added to the grape juice *before* fermentation. This gives the yeast more nourishment and increases the alcohol in the wine.

This system is called Chaptalisation or enrichment of the must (juice). It is named after Jean Antoine Chaptal, the Minister of Agriculture in the Government of Napoleon I, who suggested and authorized the process in 1801.

Malolactic fermentation

During and after the alcoholic fermentation, it is important to avoid the action of bacteria.

However, there is one exception to this rule. Lactic acid bacteria can attack the malic acid in the wine and change it into lactic acid.

Malic acid gives a harsh taste. It is the main acid in unripe apples. **Lactic acid** is light in taste. It is the main acid in milk. The result of this conversion is a softer flavour. The process produces a small amount of carbon dioxide gas, and is called the malolactic fermentation.

Types of Wine

The winemaker adapts the basic rules of fermentation to create the type of wine desired.

Wine can be classified in two ways:-

by **effervescence** : either still or sparkling
by **strength** : either light or liqueur (with added alcohol)

Styles of Wine

Each wine type can be made in one of several styles, according to:

colour : red, rosé or white
sweetness : dry, medium or sweet

A variety of wine types and styles

Methods of Production

The following sections describe the methods of fermentation used to make the different types and styles of wine.

Sparkling wines

Some of the naturally-produced carbon dioxide gas (CO_2) from the fermentation is trapped in the wine. This causes it to sparkle, instead of being released into the air as in the fermentation of still wines.

Further information on sparkling wine production is given in Chapter 8.

Liqueur wines

Most wine yeasts cease to work at about 15% alcohol. A liqueur wine has a higher degree of alcohol created by adding grape spirit (brandy) to the wine. This is either during fermentation, as in the case of port, or after fermentation, as with sherry.

Brandy and wine being run together

White wines

Grape juice, (must), is normally colourless. The colour of red wine is obtained by soaking the skins of the red grapes in the fermenting juice. If the red skins are removed at an early stage, the juice will remain colourless. Therefore white wine may be made from either red or white grapes.

Grapes for white wine are first crushed and then pressed. The skins are discarded and do not form part of the fermentation. During pressing, yeasts are washed off the grape skins into the must. The wine-maker can also decide to add more yeast to the must.

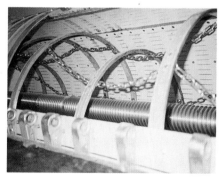

The Vaslin press. Metal hoops and chains help to break up the mass of grapes as they are pressed.

The Willmes press. A rubber bag is inflated and squeezes the grapes onto the sides of the press.

The must is then pumped into a vat. This may be made of stainless steel, cement lined with glass or tiles, or of wood.

It is then fermented at a low temperature (15 – 20°C) to preserve the delicate aromas. The fermentation lasts between two and four weeks.

Red wines

Red wine is made from the juice and skins of red grapes. The colour comes from the pigments in the skins. When the grapes reach the winery, the stalks are removed in a destalking machine and the grapes are crushed to break the skins. For red wines, both must and skins are transferred into the vat for fermentation at between 25°C and 30° C. As fermentation creates alcohol, the alcohol itself extracts first colour and then tannin from the skins.

The amount of colour and tannin in the finished wine will depend on how long the new wine is kept in contact with the skins. This can be as little as five days for light wines such as beaujolais. For more richly-flavoured wines such as top quality bordeaux, it will be about two weeks.

When colour and tannin are sufficient, the 'free run' wine is drawn from the skins into a clean vat. The skins are then pressed, yielding a further quantity of wine, known as the 'press wine'. Press wine contains higher levels of tannin, and is blended, all or in part, with the free run wine to produce the character required.

Rosé wines

Rosé wines are made from red grapes which are crushed and fermented with the skins until there is a little colour. This normally takes between 12 and 36 hours. The rosé must is then drawn off the skins and completes its fermentation at a low temperature.

Dry, medium and sweet wines

Wines with no sugar remaining in them after fermentation are known as 'dry'. This does not necessarily indicate a sour taste in the mouth, as some dry wines may have a rich and mellow flavour, eg: an Alsatian gewurztraminer (see chapter 5).
To make a medium or sweet wine, one of the following methods will be used:

(a)   Unfermented grape juice may be added to a dry wine (as with most German wine - see chapter 6).

(b)   Fermentation may deliberately be stopped while some sugar remains in the wine (as with asti spumante - see chapter 8).

(c)   In certain conditions the grapes used may be exceptionally ripe with very high sugar levels. In such cases the alcohol level of the fermenting wine will rise sufficiently to stop the yeasts working while there is plenty of sugar remaining in the must (as with sauternes - see chapter 5).

28

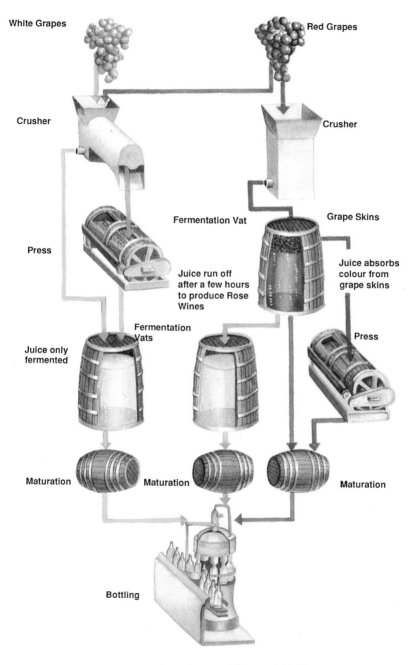

WHITE WINE

RED AND ROSE WINES

White Grapes

Red Grapes

Crusher

Crusher

Fermentation Vat

Grape Skins

Press

Juice absorbs
colour from
grape skins

Juice run off
after a few hours
to produce Rose
Wines

Fermentation
Vats

Juice only
fermented

Press

Maturation

Maturation

Maturation

Bottling

The wine making process

Treatments after Fermentation

Between the end of fermentation and the bottling of wine for sale, certain operations are usually carried out. They include:

Racking

Fermentation usually ends when the yeast has consumed all the sugar. The yeast then gradually dies and forms a sediment on the bottom of the vessel. This sediment is known as lees. The new wine is drawn from the lees into a clean vessel. This process is known as racking. Racking will take place at regular intervals until the wine is clear of sediment.

Fining

Sometimes before a racking, the wine is **fined** to ensure it is free of any haze-forming substances which might cause problems after bottling.

Substances such as bentonite, gelatine or white of egg are mixed with the wine and slowly settle through it. They attract these substances and take them to the bottom of the vat.

Bentonite is the most widely used fining at present. It is a type of powdery earth originally found at Benton in Wyoming. Curiously, its main use is in lubricating the drills used in the oil industry.

Maturation

Once again it was Louis Pasteur who first researched this process. He was asked to do this by the Emperor Napoleon III and his work drew attention for the first time to the importance of correct maturation.

Wooden casks and steel vats in a California winery

Louis Pasteur showed by experiment that wine spoils when left in contact with air. Consequently, casks are completely filled, and are topped up whenever evaporation or absorption causes a reduction in volume.

During maturation wine is allowed to rest, and the flavour to develop. In many modern wineries, maturation occurs during storage in large stainless steel vats. In some regions, such as Bordeaux, Burgundy and Rioja, many of the wines are matured in oak casks. Small oak casks are more likely to give oak flavours to the wine.

Annual Weather Conditions

This is especially important in those areas with unreliable climates where weather conditions can drastically affect the vine, the size of the crop and the final quality of the wine.

For example, in 1984 and 1985 severe cold in northern France destroyed many vines. In 1977 Bordeaux suffered a poor summer with too much rain and a lack of sun. This resulted in many rather thin, acidic red wines made from underripe grapes. In contrast in 1982, in the same region a summer heatwave produced perfectly ripe grapes and most Bordeaux châteaux produced outstanding wine.

Chapter 5
Light Wines of France

FRANCE

As far as the United Kingdom is concerned, France is the most important wine producing country in the world.

Around forty percent of all wine consumed in the UK comes from France

The main wine producing regions, as shown on the above map, are:

Bordeaux	**Burgundy**
Alsace	**Loire valley**
Rhône valley	**Provence**

Languedoc-Roussillon

The region of **Champagne** produces mainly sparkling wine and will be discussed in chapter 8.

In common with wines produced in other EC countries, French wines are divided into two categories, table wine and quality wine.

All quality wines are subject to controls on the area of production, type of grape varieties, permitted minimum alcoholic content and methods of viticulture and vinification.

Table Wine

(a)   Vin de table

French table wine may be produced anywhere in the country and is often a blend of wines from different sources.

Vins de table are simple, everyday drinking wines, usually made for early consumption.

(b)   Vin de pays

This category is for table wine with specific regional characteristics. The label on bottles of wine with this classification, will state the name of the area of production, for example, vin de pays de l'Hérault and vin de pays des Côtes de Gascogne.

Table wine labels   **Quality wine labels**

Vin de table   **Vin de pays**   **VDQS**   **AC**

Quality wine

At the heart of the regulations governing its production is the fact that the wine in the bottle must come from the geographical area stated on the label.

(a) VDQS - Vin Delimité de Qualité Supérieure

VDQS is the lower category of quality wines. The controls on vine varieties, yield and winemaking methods are stricter than for vin de pays.

(b) AC - Appellation d'Origine Contrôlée

This is the highest category of French wine, and consequently, controls for AC are the most stringent. Many wines originally given VDQS classification, such as Minervois, have since attained AC status.

FRENCH WINE REGIONS

Bordeaux

There is a long connection between Bordeaux and England. For 300 years, from 1154, Bordeaux was under English rule. In spite of political upheavals and Anglo-French wars, claret, as the red wines are called, has remained a popular wine. It kept the smuggling fraternity busy during the eighteenth and early nineteenth centuries.

Bordeaux is the largest and most important fine wine producing region of France. The production is mostly AC, plus a small amount of vin de table which does not carry the Bordeaux name.

Château Beychevelle of St. Julien in the Bordeaux region. The château was built in 1757 and is a fine example of Bordeaux architecture.

Bordeaux produces :

    (a) tannic red wines needing time to mature
    (b) lighter red wines made for early drinking
    (c) very fine sweet white wines
    (d) dry white wines, mostly, though not always, for drinking young.

The wine trade is based on the city of Bordeaux which lies on the river Garonne just before it joins the river Dordogne. Once joined, they flow as the Gironde, into the sea at the Bay of Biscay.

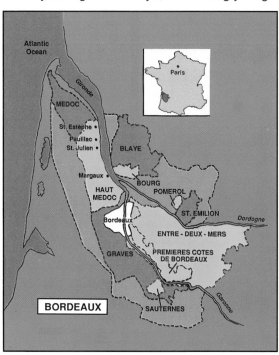

Climate

Bordeaux tends to have a mild and humid climate, influenced by the sea and rivers.

Bordeaux's winters are temperate and there are warm, long summers.

Soil

There are many types of soil but in general it is gravel, clay or sand over a sub-soil of limestone.

Grapes

The red wines are made principally from three varieties which are blended together to give the final style.

Cabernet sauvignon and cabernet franc are grapes of related varieties which give high tannin and acidity to the wine and an aroma that suggests blackcurrants.

The cabernet sauvigon produces good wine in several of the world's wine regions.

Cabernet sauvignon grapes

Merlot grapes

Merlot, a grape variety which produces higher alcohol, has a softer taste and less tannin than the cabernet grapes.

Throughout Bordeaux, more merlot is grown than cabernet. A high percentage of merlot in the blend produces wines that are easy to drink when young.

There are two Bordeaux areas which specialise in wines produced with a high proportion of cabernet. These are the Médoc and Graves. Their wines, being high in tannin and acidity, need time to mature and soften.

Of the merlot-dominated areas, the best known are St. Emilion and Pomerol.

37

Occupies @ ⅓ of all vines planted in Bordeaux

The white wines are made predominantly from a blend of two white grape varieties:

Sauvignon blanc, a grape giving high acidity and good fruit. *[handwritten: not meant for aging]*
[handwritten: gooseberries]

Sémillon, a thin skinned grape, easily attacked by noble rot, the basis of the sweet wines (see page 22). *[handwritten: Goes into Sauterne – Noble Rot likes thin skins]*

The Appellations of Bordeaux

Throughout the region the general appellation is:

Bordeaux AC
or
Bordeaux Supérieur AC

Bordeaux Supérieur AC is for wines achieving a higher degree of alcohol.

These terms apply to both red and white wines.

Many of the better red wines of Bordeaux are matured in small oak casks of 225 litres capacity, known as 'barriques'.

The other appellations relate to actual districts of production and the most important are listed as follows:

Médoc AC

As can be seen from the map, the Médoc falls into two parts. Its southern part, which produces higher quality wines, is called the Haut Médoc.

All AC wines from the Médoc are red.

The Haut Médoc is the district famous for its great, tannic, longlived wines made with a high percentage of cabernet. These wines are usually sold under the names of the châteaux where the grapes are grown.

The best vineyards of the Médoc contain a soil rich in gravel - clearly visible here.

The term 'château' (plural - châteaux) refers to a single, individually-owned, property.

In 1855 a number of the greatest wines of Bordeaux were classified. All but one of the wines came from the Haut Médoc. The exception, Château Haut Brion, was from Graves.

Out of the many hundreds of châteaux eligible, a mere 62 were classified as grands crus or great growths. The term 'cru' means vineyard.

These 62 outstanding châteaux were divided into five levels of excellence. Four châteaux (with a fifth added in 1973), the greatest of all were given the designation premier cru or first growth:

> Château Haut Brion (Graves)
> Château Lafite
> Château Latour
> Château Margaux
> Château Mouton Rothschild (1973)

A further 58 wines were classified at this time as 2nd, 3rd, 4th and 5th growths. The general term for a wine in this classification is **'cru classé'**.

Many other very good wines from châteaux in the Médoc were classified as **cru bourgeois**. This term indicates a wine of above average quality.

There are four main communes in the Médoc. A commune is roughly equivalent to a parish in England. Each of these communes has its own AC. They are:

St. Estèphe • **Pauillac** • **St. Julien** • **Margaux**

It should be remembered that a wine described simply as AC Margaux is a wine of the commune. The wine Château Margaux however, is a single vineyard wine from within that commune. Its appellation is also AC Margaux.

Graves AC

'Graves' means gravel, and the soil has given its name to the district. This area produces red and white wines and the appellation is given to both. Much wine of the region is sold simply as 'graves' without any château name.

The northern part is around the city of Bordeaux and produces mostly red wine, some of very good quality. Large quantities of dry white wine are made further south. With a few exceptions, these dry white wines are intended for early drinking.

Sauternes AC

The district of Sauternes lies 30 miles south east of Bordeaux and is surrounded by Graves. The AC here is for sweet wines only. Dry wines must be sold as bordeaux blanc.

The best sweet wines are made from grapes affected by noble rot (*pourriture noble*). The fungus pierces the skin of the grape, shrivelling it but concentrating the pulp and sugar. When gathered, these grapes yield a small amount of very concentrated juice with high sugar.

At the end of the fermentation, when the yeasts can no longer work because the alcohol has become too high, there is still a high amount of natural sweetness left in the wine.

Château d'Yquem showing part of the vineyard

The best wines of Sauternes were classified in 1855, with Château d'Yquem being named the only premier grand cru classé (first great growth). Ten other châteaux were classified as premier cru, while twelve more were named deuxième cru (second growth). **Barsac** is a commune within Sauternes. It has its own appellation for sweet wines.

Premières Côtes de Bordeaux AC

Across the river Garonne from Graves lies a small district called Premières Côtes de Bordeaux. The wines of this AC can be red or white but by far the largest amount is white, usually medium sweet in style.

Entre-Deux-Mers AC

This AC is for white wine only, most of which is dry. The wines are produced in a large area, lying between the rivers Garonne and Dordogne.

St. Emilion AC

St. Emilion itself is a very picturesque little town, built on a hill. It gives its name to the surrounding vineyards. The appellation is for red wines only.

The most important grape in the blend is the merlot, giving wines which are rich in flavour. They mature faster than the cabernet based wines of the Médoc because they have less tannin.

The vineyards were classified in 1955. Eleven châteaux are listed as premiers grands crus classes. At the top of the list are the two most famous and outstanding wines of St. Emilion: Château Ausone and Château Cheval Blanc.

Pomerol

This is a small commune on a plateau adjoining St. Emilion. Pomerol is an appellation for red wines only. The most important grape is the merlot. The most famous wine of Pomerol is Château Pétrus, where the wine is made entirely from the merlot. This tiny vineyard

Old merlot vines at Château Pétrus. The village of Pomerol is visible behind.

produces less than 4,000 cases of wine each year, and regularly commands higher prices than even 1st growths of the Médoc.

Classic bottle shapes

Burgundy

Burgundy was probably the first of the French regions to establish a reputation outside its own frontiers. This was partly due to the interest taken in viticulture by the Dukes of Burgundy. An example of this is the action of Duke Philippe the Bold in 1395. He realised that the Gamay grape did not make good wine in northern Burgundy and banished it from that area.

When the wines of Bordeaux were hardly known, burgundy was drunk by kings and courtiers and highly prized by foreign connoisseurs like Thomas Jefferson, who became President of the United States of America in 1801.

Today, demand for the greatest burgundian wines far outstrips supply.

Burgundy is situated in central France, stretching from Dijon in the north almost as far as Lyon in the south.

The region of Burgundy includes both Chablis, about 60 miles to the north west of Dijon, and the Beaujolais.

The region produces dry red and white wine and some sparkling wine. In total it produces about one third that of Bordeaux.

For historical reasons the vineyards of Burgundy are very fragmented, with many people owning a small part of a famous vineyard.

For example, Clos de Vougeot, a vineyard no larger than some Médoc châteaux, is split up into over 70 separate plots. Consequently there are many wines bearing the same name but of varying quality and differing prices.

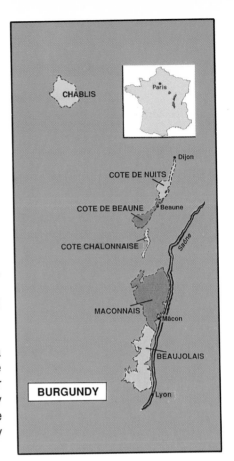

Climate

Being an inland region, Burgundy has hot summers but severe winters, with frost being a major hazard. This type of climate is called 'continental'.

Soil

The soils vary between the districts, but the most important are as follows:

Clay & limestone - Côte d'Or
Granite - Beaujolais

Grapes

Four varieties are used.

Red wines: **gamay** is the grape of Beaujolais. It produces easy drinking wine with firm acidity and little tannin. *not really for ageing*

Pinot noir makes the classic red wines of northern Burgundy. It gives an elegant wine of medium colour and high acidity. *not found in Beaujolais*

Pinot noir

Chardonnay

White wines: **chardonnay** makes all classic white burgundy. It produces wines which age very well, producing a fine bouquet and depth of flavour.

Aligoté is the lesser quality white grape. It has high acidity. Wines made from this grape are called bourgogne aligoté. *youthful drinking*

The Appellations of Burgundy

(a) Generic

Bourgogne Rouge - Bourgogne Blanc - Bourgogne Aligoté

(b) District

Some wines take the appellation of their districts, eg: Beaujolais or Côte de Beaune

(c) Commune

Just as in Bordeaux, the districts are divided into communes. Wines produced entirely from grapes grown in a particular commune can take that appellation, eg: Meursault AC and Pommard AC. Last century some burgundian communes added to their own name that of their most famous vineyard.

For example, the famous red wine vineyard of Chambertin is within the commune of Gevrey, so the commune AC is now Gevrey-Chambertin. In the same way, the commune of Puligny has added to its name that of its most famous vineyard, Montrachet, thus becoming Puligny-Montrachet.

Label samples: generic, district, commune and cru appellations of Burgundy

(d) Premier Cru

Certain vineyards producing particularly good wine have been classified as premier cru. On the bottle label, the name of the vineyard must be prefixed by the name of the commune.

(e) Grand Cru

The most special sites of all are classified as grand cru and the name of the vineyard is the appellation eg: Le Montrachet AC, La Tâche AC.

The walled vineyard of Latricières- Chambertin, a Grand Cru of the Côte de Nuits

Districts

Chablis

[handwritten: soil here called "Kimmeridgian clay"]

Chablis is a small district making white wine only from the chardonnay grape. The wines are bone dry and almost flinty. Most chablis is made and matured in stainless steel, but a few wineries still use wood.

The Côte d'Or

This long, narrow strip from Dijon to Santenay makes some of the most sought after red and white wine in the world. The best Cote d'Or wines are made with barrel maturation and age well. Its name translates as 'The Golden Slope'. The district is divided into two parts.

The Côte de Nuits in the north makes red wines from the pinot noir. This small area is home to such wines as gevrey-chambertin, nuits st. georges and chambolle-musigny.

The Côte de Beaune to the south also produces red wines, such as volnay, pommard and beaune. It also makes great white wine from the chardonnay, wines such as meursault and puligny-montrachet.

Côte Chalonnaise

[handwritten: "Region of Mercury" - Good matter of wine]

Both red and white wines are produced here. The district is sometimes called the Région de Mercurey, from the name of one of the wine making villages. The wines are similar in style to those of the Côte d'Or but are generally lighter and less long lived, as well as being less expensive.

Crémant de Bourgogne, the AC for sparkling burgundy, is the name of a wine made in the Côte Chalonnaise.

Mâconnais

[handwritten: Primarily White @ 80%]

This district produces both red and white wine, but the white wine is more important.

The white wine is made from the chardonnay, and its basic AC is Mâcon Blanc. The better white wines take the AC Mâcon Villages or add the name of the local village to Mâcon, eg: Mâcon-Lugny, Mâcon-Viré. The best known white wine is Pouilly-Fuissé.

The red wine of Mâconnais is known as Mâcon Rouge and is made from the gamay grape which may be blended with some pinot noir.

Beaujolais

In Beaujolais the gamay grape grown on granite soil produces light fruity red wines, most of which are best drunk young.

The northern part of the district produces the best quality wines, many of which are entitled to the superior AC of Beaujolais Villages. The finest beaujolais come from ten specific communes which can give their own name to the wine. These include Fleurie and Moulin-à-Vent.

10 Crus

The bulk of beaujolais comes from the southern part of the district. This area also produces most of the beaujolais nouveau, the first wine of the new vintage. It is made for immediate drinking and is released on the third Thursday of November each year.

2 G's — granite — gamay

*St Amour
Julienas
Chenas
Côte de Brouilly Chiroubles
Fleurie Morgon
Moulin-à-Vent Fleurie
Brouilly*

Alsace

Alsace is one of the loveliest parts of France. It was originally part of the Holy Roman Empire and only became French at the end of the Thirty Years War in 1648. It was annexed by Germany in 1870 and returned to France in 1919.

After such a chequered history, it is not surprising that little was known of Alsace wine, until recently. The reconstruction of the vineyards since 1919 and the development of her fine wines are a tribute to the foresight and determination of the wine makers.

Alsace villages line the foothills of the Vosges mountains.

Alsace lies in north eastern France on the border with Germany. It is bounded by the Rhine to the east and is almost separated from France by the Vosges mountains to the west.

Almost all Alsace wines are white and, with one or two exceptions, all of them are dry.

Climate

Alsace has a continental climate, with hot summers and severe winters. However it is an exceptionally dry and sunny region. This is caused by the Vosges mountains which shelter the vineyards from the rain-bearing winds blowing across northern France. The vineyards are situated on the eastern foothills of the Vosges facing south or south east, which therefore benefit from the sun.

This sheltered position means that the grapes ripen well in spite of the latitude and, as a result, the alcohol is a good even strength.

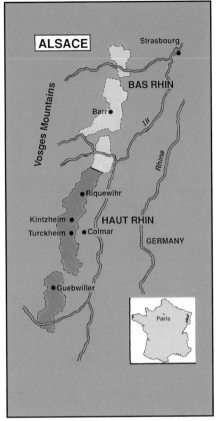

Soil

There is no predominant soil type.

Grapes

There are a number of grape varieties in Alsace, however four of the most important are: **riesling, gewurztraminer, sylvaner and pinot blanc.**

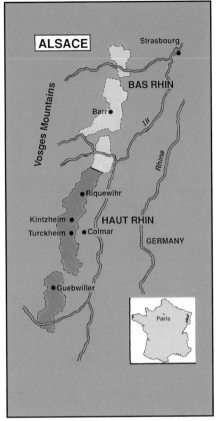

A selection of prominent Alsace wines

Only 6% of the total production in Alsace is red and the grape used is pinot noir.

The appellation for most wines is **AC Alsace.** The best vineyards are being reclassified as AC Alsace Grand Cru. Unlike most other quality wine regions of France, the most prominent name shown on the label is usually the grape variety and not the district of production.

All AC Alsace wine is bottled in the region in special tall, slim, green bottles. These are called the 'flûtes d'Alsace'.

Loire Valley

Before the English acquired Bordeaux, the Loire was their main source of French wine. After this trade disappeared, the Dutch became the major customers for Loire wines. They had a great influence on the styles of wine made. It was the Dutch who introduced white grapes rather than the traditional red ones.

After the Franco-Dutch war of 1672, Loire winemakers had to look for local markets and it was not until after 1945 that their wines again became well known outside France.

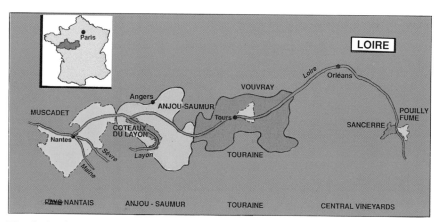

The Loire is the longest river in France. It rises in the Massif Central and finally reaches the sea at Nantes just south of Brittany.

The four main wine areas lie between the Atlantic and the centre of France. The Loire produces all styles of wine; dry, medium and sweet white wines, sparkling wines, rosé and red wines.

Climate

Climatic conditions in a region as large as the Loire Valley vary considerably. Around Nantes the influence of the sea creates a mild, damp climate, while inland the weather patterns are continental.

The Château de Chenonceau perched above one of the tributaries of the Loire river.

Soil

There are many different types of soils, chalk and clay being most prominent.

Grapes

The most important grapes for white wines are:

muscadet   **chenin blanc**   **sauvignon blanc**

luscious dessert wine

For red and rosé wines the important grape is: **cabernet franc**

Gamay

The Loire Appellations

There are four main sub-regions and a number of appellations within each. Starting from the Brittany coast and working inland, they are:

Vin de Nantes

This is the home of muscadet, one of the largest selling quality wines in the UK. Muscadet is the name of the grape as well as the wine. It is a dry, fruity, white wine made from grapes grown around the town of Nantes. Muscadet is usually drunk young and fresh.

Some better quality muscadet is bottled directly from the sediment produced by the wine's fermentation. This gives more intense fruit and sometimes a faint prickle of CO_2. This wine will be labelled muscadet sur lie (literally 'on the lees' - see chapter 4).

Muscadet vines in the Nantais

Anjou-Saumur

Saumur produces AC white wines, mostly dry, from the chenin blanc grape. The soil in Saumur is a type of volcanic chalk called tufa. The combination of this tufa chalk and the chenin blanc produces a very popular sparkling saumur.

Côteaux du Layon produces sweet and medium sweet wine from the chenin blanc. In this sheltered area influenced by the Loire and its tributary the Layon, the chenin blanc can be affected by noble rot.

The whole district of Anjou-Saumur is the source of the medium sweet anjou rosé made mainly from the groslot grape. If the wine is made from cabernet it is called cabernet d'anjou.

Touraine

In Touraine the still wines may be red, white or rosé, and some sparkling wine is also made.

The most famous appellation is that of Vouvray. Though made from one white grape the chenin blanc, the widest variety of styles is produced. They may be dry, medium or sweet, still or sparkling. The sweet wines are the finest and most long lived. The label does not always reveal the style of wine in the bottle.

In Vouvray, as in Saumur, the soil is tufa chalk, and some good sparkling vouvray is produced.

Another appellation of some importance is that of Sauvignon de Touraine, for dry white wines made from that grape variety.

Central Vineyards

These are so-called because they are in the centre of France. Here growing on a special form of limestone and clay, the sauvignon produces some of its most famous, dry, smoky wines.

The appellations are Pouilly Fumé ('fumé means smoky) and Sancerre.

The hilltop village of Sancerre overlooks the surrounding vineyards.

The Rhône valley is one of the oldest wine producing regions of France. It is certain that wine existed there by about 600 BC, and it is believed that the steep terraced vineyards of the northern Rhône were the earliest French vine plantations.

During the period that the popes lived at Avignon, from 1309 to 1378, Pope John XXII built his new palace. He did not live long to enjoy it, dying in 1334 the year after Châteauneuf du Pape (the Pope's new palace) was complete.

The famous incomplete Pont d'Avignon on the Rhône river

Over the centuries the strong Rhône wines were often used to blend with lighter ones from further north. In recent years, though, their quality has begun to be appreciated.

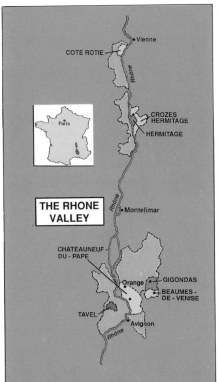

THE RHONE VALLEY

The wine region of the Rhône valley starts south of Lyon at Vienne and extends south to Avignon, a distance of about 140 miles.

The area is divided into two parts, with the gap in the vineyards around Montélimar, the town famous for its nougat.

The northern and southern Rhône districts have different climates, soils and grape varieties, leading to quite different styles of wine.

The General Rhône Appellation

The general appellation is **AC Côtes du Rhône,** and almost all the wine produced is red.

The Northern Rhône

In this part of the region the valley is narrow and the river flows between steep cliffs.

The vines are grown on terraces, mostly so narrow and steep that no machinery can be used and all the work has to be done by hand.

Consequently, wine in the northern Rhône is expensive to produce. These slopes produce dry, long-lived red wines and a small amount of fine white.

Terraced vineyards of the northern Rhône.

Climate

The northern Rhône has a continental climate with cold winters and short summers.

The main problem is the Mistral, a powerful, cold wind which blows down the valley from the north. Vines cannot be planted on the most exposed sites.

Soil

To resist the strength of the Mistral wind, many vines in the northern Rhône are trained on 'wigwam' supports to anchor them into the ground.

The soil in general is predominantly granite with some sandstone.

Grapes

The red grape variety of the northern Rhône is the **syrah.** It produces big, fruity wines with high tannin when young, giving the wines a great ageing potential.

Northern Rhône Appellations

The northern Rhône is split into a number of districts, each with its own AC.

The most important red wine districts are:

Côte Rôtie
Hermitage.

[handwritten: Chateau Grillet, St Joseph, — Crozes - Hermitage]

Hermitage is surrounded by the larger district of Crozes Hermitage which makes less intense wines.

The Southern Rhône

In the south the Rhône valley has broadened out. There are no steep cliffs, only a wide, flat plain marked by outcrops of large stones, and it is difficult to realise that this is the same river valley.

The wines here are mainly red, with some rosé and a small amount of white wine.

In contrast to the northern area which makes fine wine in small amounts, this is the home of a large quantity of average quality drinking wine plus a few great ones.

Climate

This southern part of the Rhône valley enjoys a Mediterranean climate with mild winters and hot summers and autumns. Rainfall is low, mostly falling in spring or autumn.

Here again the Mistral is a problem, and everywhere cypress trees and fences have been erected as wind breaks.

Soil

There is a variety of soils. The sub-soil is limestone with a covering of sand and large stones in the finest areas.

Grape varieties

In contrast to the northern Rhône, the AC laws in the southern Rhône permit many different red and white grape varieties. The former include grenache, syrah, cinsault and mourvèdre. The most important of these is the grenache. However, even this grape is almost always blended with others.

Southern Rhône Appellations

Apart from the general AC Côtes du Rhône, there is an area, marked on the map, containing 16 villages which produce superior wine.

Wines from this area are given the AC Cotes du Rhone Villages. If a wine comes from just one of these villages, then it may include the name in the appellation, for example:

AC Côtes du Rhone St Gervais.

Apart from the Appellations of Côtes du Rhône and Côtes du Rhône Villages, all quality wines take the name of the district. The most important are:-

Tavel - producing dry, full bodied rosé wines. These rosés are made by vinifying red and white grapes together. *V. Alcoholic powerful stuff*

Other rosés are made from red grapes only - see Chapter 2.

Beaumes de Venis - dessert wine

Gigondas - one of the original côtes du rhône villages. The wine is sufficiently good for it to be given its own AC for red wines. This was awarded in 1971.

Châteauneuf-du-Pape - a very large district containing many properties. The production is almost entirely red.   As stated earlier, the area takes its name from the castle built by the Pope, which is now overlooking the village.

Primarily Red up to 13 grape varieties used in production

Many of the vineyards are covered with pudding stones which reflect the heat on to the grapes ripening them very thoroughly.

The alcohol levels of these wines are high, the minimum required being 12.5% .

Pudding stones covering a vineyard in the southern Rhône. The land is typically flat.

Grenache main grape variety also added Syrah Cinsault Mourvèdre

Provence

This area lies to the south east of Avignon and finishes at the Italian border.

The styles of wine are mainly dry rosé and red.

The climate is Mediterranean and there are considerable variations in the soil.

Grape varieties are similar to those in the southern Rhône.

Main quality wine districts are AC Côtes de Provence and Coteaux d'Aix en Provence, both producing large quantities of red and rosé wines.

The Mediterranean vineyards of Provence produce mellow dry rosé and red wines.

Languedoc-Roussillon

This area is a great arc spreading from the Spanish border to the Rhône estuary and produces one third of all French wines. It is commonly known as the Midi.

In the past it has been the source of cheap and plentiful, basic drinking wine. Today there is greater emphasis on quality and many good wines are being produced.

Once again the grape varieties are as in the southern Rhône. Important appellations include Fitou, Côtes du Roussillon, Corbières and Minervois.

This is a major area for production of vins de pays, the main areas being Gard, Hérault, Aude and Pyrenées Orientales.

Some of these wines are made from local grapes, while others are made from vines introduced into the area from other parts of France, eg: cabernet sauvignon and chardonnay.

High-yielding vin de table vineyards are seen here on flat land in the Languedoc-Roussillon. Today such inferior sites are being abandoned in favour of hillside locations.

Other French wine Producing Regions

In addition to those already covered, there are a number of other smaller quality regions. These include the ACs of Jura and Savoie in eastern France, Bergerac, Cahors, Jurançon and Madiran in south western France, and Haut Poitou, a VDQS region situated around Poitiers in central France.

Chapter 6
Other Light Wines of the European Community

Germany

The German vineyards lie in the southern half of the country close to the northern limit for wine production. The climate, which is cool and damp during the growing season, may be described as marginal. In some years the grapes do not ripen fully.

These conditions produce wines which are often low in alcohol and high in acidity. Such wines, when made dry, can taste unpalatably sharp.

To achieve balance, the alcohol may be given a limited boost by chaptalisation and if a portion of the grape juice is left unfermented, it will provide sweetness and fruit to balance the acidity. This use of unfermented sweet juice, or 'Süssreserve', has given to German wines a unique balance of grapy sweetness, light weight and refreshing acidity.

In a climate where degrees of ripeness will vary greatly from year to year, even in the best vineyards, it has been found necessary to evolve a system of quality grading which is dependent on grape ripeness rather than vineyard location.

This is in contrast to the French system in which vineyards with an established reputation are given the same quality status from year to year, irrespective of climatic variation.

The 50th parallel (50°N) runs through the estate of Schloss Johannisberg in the Rheingau, one of the finest German vineyards.

The German wine production regions are shown on the map.

These regions are grouped around the river Rhine and its major tributaries, which include the Mosel.

The wines produced within Germany are classified into two categories, table wine and quality wine, each with two subdivisions.

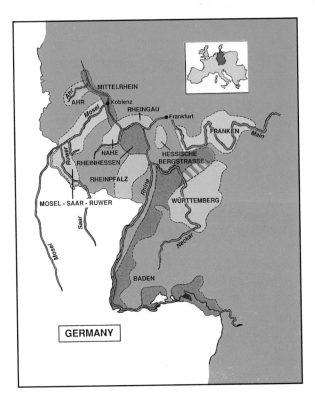

Table Wine

(a)   Deutscher Tafelwein

If the wine has been made from grapes grown in Germany, the label states 'Deutscher Tafelwein'.

NB: The term 'Tafelwein' on its own indicates that a wine is blended with imported wine from other countries in the European Community. These wines, although often made in Germany, are not German wines as such.

(b)   Deutscher Landwein

This classification is similar to French "vin de pays". It is a category of tafelwein, a regional wine made from grapes that are a little riper (ie: with greater potential alcohol) at harvest time. Landwein is made drier than many other German wines, and will be labelled either:

Trocken   meaning 'dry'
or
Halbtrocken   meaning 'semi-dry'.

Quality Wine

Quality wines, known in Germany as **Qualitätswein**, are also divided into two categories.

(a) QbA (Qualitätswein bestimmte Anbaugebiete) *Designated wine region*

The wine label will state either Qualitätswein bA or show the initials QbA. 'Bestimmte Anbaugebiete' means 'designated quality wine region'.

Qualitätswein comes from one of ~~eleven~~ *thirteen* quality wine regions or Anbaugebiete which are marked on the map. The region must always be stated clearly on the label.

Each of these eleven regions is divided into districts. Districts are known as Bereiche, and a single one as a **Bereich**. A wine may be named after one of these, such as Bereich Bernkastel in the middle Mosel and Bereich Johannisberg in the Rheingau.

Each Bereich is itself subdivided into Grosslagen. A **Grosslage** consists of a group of vineyards producing wine of similiar character. Famous examples are Niersteiner Gutes Domtal and Piesporter Michelsberg.

The smallest subdivision is the **Einzellage** or individual vineyard. Examples are Bernkasteler Doktor and Johannisberger Hölle.   It is not possible to distinguish between a Grosslage or an Einzellage, without specialized knowledge.

(b) QmP (Qualitätswein mit Prädikat)

QmP wines are QbA wines with extra qualities, mainly associated with later harvesting. These wines may not be chaptalised.

Within QmP there are six different categories. The categories, in ascending order of natural grape sugar at time of harvesting, are as follows:

Kabinett   Made from grapes harvested at the normal time but with higher natural grape sugar. These are the lightest and most delicate of the QmP wines.

Spätlese   Made from grapes which are harvested late and are therefore riper. A more intense and concentrated style.

Auslese   Made from individually selected, extra ripe bunches of late-harvested grapes. The wine is normally medium sweet in style, with a good balancing acidity.

Beerenauslese   Made from carefully selected, late-harvested overripe individual grapes, normally affected by noble rot. The wines have both a considerable residual sweetness and balancing acidity.

(Ice Wine) doesn't occur every year. luscious dessert wine

Eiswein   Made from grapes which have been picked during the first snowfalls and pressed while still frozen. A rare wine of great richness.

state of berries

Trockenbeerenauslese Made from individually selected grapes which have been so infected with noble rot that they have shrivelled like raisins.

| Deutscher Tafelwein | Deutscher Landwein | QbA | QmP |

German Wine Labels

German wine labels look complicated, but in fact are both simple and logical. In the case of the QmP illustrated above, the actual wine name consists of four words:

Winkeler	- the village of origin is Winkel
Hasensprung	- the name of the vineyard
Riesling	- the grape variety
Auslese	- the quality status

Quality Control Testing

Each QbA or QmP must pass a quality control test at the appropriate state testing centre. The tests involve both a laboratory analysis and tasting.

On passing the test the wine is given an official quality control number (known as the Amtliche Prüfungsnummer or AP Nr). This must be shown on the label. Should the wine fail either test, the best it can hope for is to be sold as 'Deutscher Tafelwein'.

Geographical Location

The German wine producing regions lie between latitudes 48° and 52° North, which includes an area just outside the normal limit of 50°. The 50th parallel actually runs through the vineyard of Schloss Johannisberg in the Rheingau.

Climate

The climate is cool for a wine producing region, with winters being very cold. Frost is always a danger, with vineyard areas so far from the sea. Summers can be warm and in good years late, warm autumns help ripen the grapes.

Grape Varieties

Many grape varieties are grown, but three are of particular importance:

Riesling

Widely regarded as the best German wine grape, this is a late ripening variety with a balance of flavours and strong acidity. It makes wines capable of producing concentrated flavours when mature. Riesling accounts for 20% of the German vineyard area.

Riesling grapes

Silvaner

This is a traditional Germanic variety, giving a much higher yield than riesling, but usually a much softer wine. Approximately 8% of the German vineyards are planted with silvaner.

Müller-thurgau

An early ripening variety developed by Professor Müller from the Swiss canton of Thurgau, in 1882. Its yields are high and it is now the widest planted grape in Germany.

Müller-thurgau grapes

Although these are the most important grapes, there are a number of other vine varieties grown within Germany, including kerner and gewürztraminer. Their names are sometimes seen on wine labels. Mono-Muskat, Scheurebe,

Viticulture

The secret of a successful ripening of grapes so far north is knowledge of local climatic conditions. Vines are planted on south facing slopes near rivers, on mountain slopes or in areas protected by forests or ranges of hills.

Vinification

In many years, the northerly climate can result in grapes which are high in acidity but low in natural sugar, owing to lack of sun. If all the sugar is fermented out to dryness the wine is often very harsh with acidity. To overcome this problem, sterile, unfermented grape juice is usually added to the wine just before it is bottled. This grape juice is called 'Süssreserve' which translates literally as "sweet reserve". Its use balances any harsh, overacidic taste with a touch of sweetness and fruit.

Main Wine Producing Areas

German wine styles fall into two principal categories, **Mosel** and **Rhine**.

Mosel

Mosel wines are pale in colour, light in body and with a crisp elegance. They are sold in tall green bottles.

The vineyards lie on the steep, south facing slopes of the river Mosel and its tributaries, the Saar and the Ruwer. The most important soil is slate. The warmth of the sun reflected from the river and the slate, helps to ripen the grapes.

The best Mosel wines come from the riesling grown on slate soil. The most famous area is the Middle Mosel, with wine villages such as Bernkastel and Piesport.

Both quality wines and table wines are produced. Quality wines quote the QbA region Mosel-Saar-Ruwer; the table wines are known as Mosel Tafelwein.

Slate topsoil covers the steep slopes of the Mosel vineyards.

Rhine

Rhine wines are fuller in style and are traditionally sold in brown bottles. These wines are often referred to by the British as 'hock', a name derived from the village of Hocheim, in the Rheingau, the source of Queen Victoria's favourite wine.

The soils of the Rhine are very varied.

The best-known quality regions in the UK market are Rheingau, Rheinhessen, Rheinpfalz and Nahe.

The riesling is the most important grape in the Rheingau and Nahe. Important wines from the Rheingau include Rüdesheimer Berg and Schloss Vollrads. Wines from the Nahe are often said to be halfway in style between the Mosel and the Rhine.

Wooded hilltops shelter the vineyards of the prestigious Rüdesheimer Berg estate in the Rheingau.

Müller-thurgau and silvaner, as well as many newer varieties, are widely planted in the Rheinhessen. The finest vineyards in this region are around Nierstein and Oppenheim. Here the grapes are mainly riesling.

The Rheinpfalz, also known as the Palatinate, is protected by the Haardt mountains. It is the warmest and driest of these four regions and produces the fullest flavoured wines.

Regional Wines

A number of regional wines are produced under a quality wine label. They must be of QbA status only, never QmP. The most famous of these is liebfraumilch.

Liebfraumilch originated from a vineyard at Worms in the Rheinhessen, and it must come from one of the four Rhine regions, Rheinhessen, Rheinpfalz, Rheingau or Nahe. The law requires it to be soft, fruity and easy to drink.

Other Quality Regions

The other six quality wine regions are, from the north, Ahr (mostly red wine), Mittelrhein, Franken, Hessische Bergstrasse, Württemberg, and Baden which stretches down to the Swiss border.

Italy

Cultivation of the vine was developed in Italy by two different peoples. The Greeks brought their knowledge to the south through Sicily and the toe of Italy. Amazed by the ease with which vines grew everywhere, the Greeks named Italy 'Oenotria', land of the vine.

To the north of Rome there lived a people called the Etruscans. Even today little is known about the Etruscans who were destroyed by the growing power of the Romans, but it is known they also made wine.

The Alps form a backdrop to a vineyard in Barbaresco, in north west Italy.

At first the Romans imported wine. Greek wines were considered the finest. Gradually, however, they developed vine growing themselves and spread their knowledge, bringing vines and wines to all parts of the world where their legions were stationed.

It seems fitting, therefore, that even today Italy is in most years the largest producer, making one fifth of the world's wine.

Quality Grading

Table Wine - Vino da Tavola

This category is the equivalent of the French vin de table.

Although in many cases these are the simplest and cheapest of wines, some of the most interesting wines are sold as Vino da Tavola.

Quality Wine

(a)   DOC (Denominazione di Origine Controllata)

This is the Italian equivalent of the French AC and was introduced in 1963.

DOC on the label guarantees-

1.   that the wine has been produced in the named vineyard area

2.   that methods of production in the vineyard and the winery have been specified.

(b)   DOCG (Denominazione di Origine Controllata e Garantita)

This category has been reserved for a few wines that have been subjected to even stricter controls. Each bottle carries a government seal.

Examples of DOCG wines include barolo and chianti.

Recently more Italian producers have aged their best wines in barriques. These include the top vini da tavola such as Tignanello, a fine red wine produced in Tuscany by Antinori.

Climate

Italy lies between latitudes 37° N at the toe and 47°N in the Alps. This means that there is quite a variation in climate along the length of the country, but overall the climate is much more consistent from year to year than in Germany or northern France.

Grape Varieties

An enormous number of grape varieties are grown. They can be divided into three groups.

(a)   Those grapes which are native to Italy. The most important native red grapes are:

nebbiolo
sangiovese
barbera
lambrusco

Nebbiolo

Barbera

Important white varieties are -

verdicchio
trebbiano
malvasia

Sangiovese

Verdicchio

(b)   Those grapes that were originally brought from other countries, but length of time has made them traditional. Examples of this type are pinot grigio (white) and merlot (red) which were introduced at the time of Napoleon.

(c)   Finally there are those whose rise to prominence has been recent, such as chardonnay (white) and cabernet sauvignon (red).

Italian Wine Labels

Naming of Wines

DOC and DOCG wines must always state the area of origin, eg: barolo, frascati. However, in some DOC names, the region is qualified by the name of the grape as well; examples being barbera d'alba and merlot di pramaggiore.

For vini da tavola (table wines), names may refer to the grape used (lambrusco), or may be an invented 'brand' name, such as Tignanello or Sassicaia.

Other words on the label may include:

Secco	-	Dry
Riserva	-	Good quality and aged for a longer period than normal.
Classico	-	The heartland of a district, producing the finest wines.
Superiore	-	Higher minimum quality requirements.
Vecchio	-	Old
Abboccato/ Amabile	-	Medium sweet
Dolce	-	Sweet
Annata	-	Year
Vendemmia	-	Vintage

Consorzio Seal

A consorzio is a voluntary association of producers within a specific area. Sometimes the symbol of a consorzio appears on the bottle, indicating very careful control over and above

The black cockerel or 'gallo nero' symbol of Chianti Classico

the DOC requirements. Each consorzio has its own symbol, for example the black rooster of Chianti Classico.

Principal Wines

Barolo DOCG - a full bodied red wine with great ageing potential. Barolo is made from the nebbiolo grape grown in the vineyards around the village of Barolo in Piemonte. It must be aged for a minimum of 3 years.

Barbaresco DOCG - is a red wine from the nebbiolo grape grown in Piemonte. Similar to barolo in style, barbaresco matures rather earlier.

Valpolicella DOC - a red wine, usually quite light in colour and style, this wine is made from a mixture of grapes grown in vineyards near Verona, in the northeast.

Bardolino DOC - a light red wine, similar to valpolicella and made from the same grapes. It is grown on the eastern shores of lake Garda, just west of Valpolicella.

Soave DOC - a very dry but fruity white wine named after the commune of Soave near Verona.

Lambrusco - a lightly sparkling and usually medium sweet, pale red wine from the grape of the same name. Made in central Italy, it is sometimes vinified into a white wine.

Verdicchio - dry white wine made from the verdicchio grape. It is a fresh, fruity wine with a crisp acidity and a pleasantly bitter aftertaste. The DOC wines include the name of area after the grape name, for example verdicchio dei castelli di jesi, and are grown in the province of Marche on the east coast.

Chianti DOCG - a red wine produced in Tuscany and made from a mixture of grape varieties, the most important being the sangiovese. It can vary in style from light red wines made for early drinking to well aged wines with great depth of flavour. There is a classico area. Since 1984 chianti has been designated DOCG.

Orvieto DOC - a white wine made in Umbria. Traditionally orvieto was abboccato, or semi sweet, and such styles are still available, but today most orvieto is made as secco, or dry.

Frascati DOC - is a white wine usually dry, although sweeter styles are permitted under the DOC. It is made just south of Rome, and has a medium full, mellow flavour.

Southern Italy

Southern Italian wine regions have been more noted for quantity than quality. Much of the wine is consumed locally, or is used as the base wine for the making of vermouth (see Chapter 9).

Substantial improvements have taken place in recent years and increasing amounts of better quality wine from this area are being shipped overseas. Particularly true of this current trend are the wines of Sicily.

Spain

Spain has more land under vines than any other country, but ranks only third in production terms.

Apart from sherry, Spain produces large quantities of light wines. These are mostly dry, and can be red, rosé or white.

Quality Grading

Vino de mesa is Spanish table wine.

DO (Denominación de Origen) is the Spanish equivalent of the French AC and guarantees the geographical origin of the wine. There are also rules for strict controls on viticulture, vinification, and alcohol content, establishing standards of quality.

The system was introduced in 1970, and local councils were created to administer it. Each council is known as a **consejo regulador**.

By 1989, the number of DO regions had increased to over thirty.

DOC (Denominación de Origen Calificada) is a higher quality grade introduced in 1991 initially for the wines of Rioja.

Grape Varieties

The most important Spanish varieties for red wines are **tempranillo** and **garnacha**. For white wines, the grapes are **viura** and **airén**.

In some regions experiments are taking place with noble grapes from France such as **cabernet sauvignon** and **chardonnay**.

Main Regions

Rioja DOC

This wine growing region is situated in northern Spain along the banks of the river Ebro. It is named after a tributary of the Ebro, the Rio Oja.

In Rioja, as in Bordeaux, many wines are matured in oak casks of 225 litres.

The region is divided into three disticts, Rioja Alta, Rioja Alavesa and Rioja Baja, and the main centre is Logroño. Most riojas are a blend of wines from the different districts. The two most important red grapes here are tempranillo and garnacha.

After fermentation most wines are matured in oak, which gives a traditional flavour to the wine. **Reserva** wines have had a longer maturation than the standard riojas and **gran reservas** are the finest wines with the longest maturation periods of all. However, today some rioja wines are made without any wood maturation.

Although rioja is mainly red, good white rioja is made from the viura grape.

Navarra DO

Navarra lies to the north of Rioja and has a cool, temperate climate. It produces red and white wine similar in style to rioja, but often lighter.

La Mancha DO

This area is a vast arid plateau south of Madrid. The climate is extreme, scorching in the summer and very cold during the winter.

La Mancha is the largest area of production in Spain. Though much of its wine is used to make Spanish brandy, it also produces white and red DO wines which are steadily improving in quality.

Valdepeñas DO

Joining La Mancha to the south lies the small DO region of Valdepeñas. Here the soil is stony over a chalk sub-soil. Much of the wine is of basic quality for drinking young. A few producers are experimenting with cask ageing and they produce a style of wine similar to that of rioja.

Penedés DO

Most of Spain's quality sparkling wine is produced in this region, which lies west-south-west of Barcelona.

It is also a DO region producing a range of red, white and rosé light wines.

Most are fresh, fruity and are intended for drinking young.

There is also experimentation in this area. Some growers are planting

The hilly region of Penedés produces a great range of wine styles.

imported grape varieties such as cabernet, chardonnay and pinot noir.

The best known of these wineries is Bodegas Miguel Torres.

Valencia DO

Valencia is one of a number of DO regions east of La Mancha and stretching to the coast. Valencia produces mainly red and rosé wine, as well as a small quantity of white. Other major crops include oranges and almonds.

Montilla-Moriles DO

The wines of Montilla-Moriles, commonly known as montilla, are often likened to sherry. There are several points of similarity. Montilla produces a range of styles including dry, medium and sweet (cream) wines.

Some of the production is fortified, but the majority of that which is exported to the UK is light wine, at an alcohol level of under 15% vol.

Portugal

Portugal comprises a narrow coastal plain, rising steeply to mountainous inland regions. South westerly winds from the Atlantic bring rain during the winter months and the summers tend to be very hot. Red and white wines are made. There is also a large production of slightly sparkling medium sweet rosé.

Quality grading

As with other E.C. countries, the wines of Portugal are divided into table wines called vinho de mesa, and quality wines. Quality wines come from demarcated areas and are labelled regiao demarcada or denominacao de origem.

Main Regions

Vinho Verde

'Vinho Verde' means, literally, 'green wine'. This does not refer to the colour of the wine itself, but to its character.

In Vinho Verde, vines are trained high. A canopy of leaves shelters the grapes from the sun, reducing its ripening effect and resulting in wines with moderate alcohol and fresh acidity.

Unlike most other wines from hot climates, vinho verde wines have fresh acidity and moderate alcohol. They are best consumed when young.

Vinho verde comes from the province of Minho-é-Douro in northern Portugal. The vines are trained high. More red wine than white wine is produced, but the red is only available in Portugal, as it appeals only to local tastes.

Dão

The Dão region is named after a river. The Dão is south of the Douro valley, in northern central Portugal, a wild and beautiful country with terraced vineyards on granite slopes.

The wines are mainly red and spend a long time maturing in wooden casks. Some white dão is also made.

Bairrada

A fairly recently demarcated region south of Oporto and near the coast, making some good red wine, which is sometimes given several years of age, both in wood and in bottle.

'Garrafeira' is a term sometimes seen on Portuguese wine labels. It indicates a wine which has been aged for a significantly longer period than usual.

Greece   *High alcohol*   *Chateau Carras*
Poutari — Good quality wines

Greece is one of the oldest wine producing countries of the world.

In ancient times, Greek wines were considered to be the finest. Today, the best known wine is retsina, a white wine vinified with a small amount of pine resin added to the must. Retsina is made in vast quantities, and is very much an acquired taste.

Greece also produces red, white and rosé wines, and sweet wines such as muscat de samos and the red liqueur wine, mavrodaphne.

Believe in viniculture

The modern winery of Achaia Clauss, from Patras in southern Greece, exports a variety of styles including sweet liqueur wines and non-resinated light wines.

England and Wales

England has a tradition of wine making stretching back to Roman times.

Following the dissolution of the monasteries by Henry VIII between 1536 and 1539, some vineyards survived.

Since the 1950s a small percentage of farmland in the southern half of the country has been planted with vines.

Suitable soils exist for growing grapes; the problem lies in the erratic climate which often provides too much rain and too little sun. Chaptalisation, to boost the alcohol level, is common. English wine is classed as table wine. It is almost entirely white.

In exceptional years the grapes ripen successfully and good wines are produced with clean fruit flavours and crisp acidity. Among the more common grape varieties used are: müller-thurgau, the hybrid seyval blanc, and a number of recently developed German varieties including huxelrebe and reichensteiner.

(c) 400 vineyards in Eng & Wales.

74

Chapter 7
Light Wines from
Outside the European Community

Romania produces
white wine
Bulgaria — ⅓ of UK wines

CENTRAL AND
SOUTHEASTERN
EUROPE

Riesling vs. rizling

Several of the countries in Central and South Eastern Europe produce wine from a single vine variety called either:

welschriesling (Austria)

laski rizling (Yugoslavia)

olasz rizling (Hungary)

depending on the country of origin.

Before the enforcement of European legislation in the spring of 1988, the laski rizling and the olasz rizling were known as laski riesling and olasz riesling. These names may be found on bottles labelled before 1988.

It is very important to remember that this vine is neither the genuine Rhine riesling of Germany and Alsace, nor a related variety.

Switzerland

Little Swiss wine is seen outside the country. The styles are mainly white, or light red.

Austria

The wine regions are in the eastern part of Austria, around Vienna. Well over 80% is white wine, much of it made from a local grape, the grüner veltliner.

As Austria is a German-speaking country, wine labels use German terms such as Qualitatswein, Kabinett, etc. In general these mean the same as they mean in Germany. However, on account of the warmer climate, the wines are richer and fuller. *V. different than German wines*

New bottling / label

The largest areas are Lower Austria or Niederösterreich and Burgenland, the northern part of which is famous for its sweet dessert wine.

Bulgaria

Bulgaria has a very old tradition of wine-making dating back to pre-Roman times. In five centuries of occupation the Turks failed to destroy this.

Wine production has been completely modernised since 1949, under the direction of the State.

The use of western European vine varieties and careful oak ageing has contributed to expanding exports of Bulgarian wines in the 1980's.

Bulgaria produces large quantities of red and dry white wines, some of which are very good.

Most Bulgarian wine exported to Britain is produced from western European grape varieties, such as cabernet sauvignon, chardonnay and merlot.

In the late 1980's, Bulgarian regional wines of superior quality have been exported. Some have used indigenous grape varieties, or have been matured in small oak casks.

Reserve — seen extra ageing in oak casks
Controliran — appellation controlée equivalent

Hungary

Hungary has made wine throughout its turbulent history.

Hungary is mainly flat. Its landscape includes the Great Plain and the largest lake in Europe, lake Balaton. The climate is continental with cold winters but, during the growing season, is ideal, having little frost and abundant sunshine. Hungary produces a great amount of red and white wine of sound but not fine quality.

Much Hungarian wine exported to Britain is white and is made from the olasz rizling. However, as in Bulgaria, some French varieties such as cabernet sauvignon and merlot are now being grown to produce varietal wine.

Two famous wines are found in northern Hungary:

Bulls Blood of Eger, or Egri Bikaver, is made in the district surrounding the town and fortress of Eger. Bulls Blood takes its name from a 16th Century legend. This tells of a Turkish army which beseiged Eger. The women regularly took wine to the soldiers manning the battlements. The soldiers fought so bravely that the Turks came to believe that their enemies had been drinking the blood of bulls.

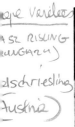

Old bottles of tokaji in Hungarian cellars.

The world famous sweet wine, tokaji aszú, which has been famous since the time of the crusades, is made in the north east of the country, near the border with Czechoslovakia. Hot summers with long autumns, together with close proximity to the river Tisza, create good conditions for noble rot.

Many varieties of tokaji are made, which may be dry or medium, but tokaji aszú is the famous traditional sweet wine. Like the best sweet wines of Sauternes, tokaji aszú is capable of ageing for decades.

77

Yugoslavia

This is the largest of the Balkan countries, bordering on Austria in the north, and Albania and Greece in the south.

The grape harvest in Lutomer.

Yugoslavia makes many styles of wine. Its best known export if Yugoslav laski rizling, which first arrived in the UK in 1947. It is a medium dry white wine.

Lutomer laski rizling is grown only around the town of Lutomer in northern Yugoslavia near the borders with Austria and Hungary. Here the influence of the Alps gives a temperate climate suitable to the production of white wine.

Other Mediterranean Countries

Cyprus

Cyprus makes red, white and rosé wines, and also liqueur wines, such as commandaria. The main production area is around the Troodos mountains.

North Africa

The north African countries once made large amounts of wine. Algeria gained its independence from France in 1962, and since then production has fallen. The best wines are red and come from Morocco, and smaller amounts are being made in Algeria and Tunisia.

Other Wine Producing Countries

A considerable volume of wine of all types is produced in the USSR, particularly in the republics bordering the Black Sea (Moldavia, Ukraine and Georgia).

Wine is also produced in Romania, Turkey, Lebannon, Israel, India, China and Japan

Since the late 17th Century there has been an increasing amount of wine made in many of the new world countries.

The wines are mostly made from noble grape varieties originally imported from Europe. They are usually labelled by the grape variety used, rather than by region or vineyard name. This is called varietal labelling.

The most popular varietals in recent years have been cabernet sauvignon and chardonnay.

South Africa

Wine has been made in South Africa since 1659, after the original Dutch settlers planted vines in the Cape region, still today the centre of production.

South Africa now has a well-controlled production of red, white and liqueur wines.

Important vine varieties include cabernet sauvignon and pinotage for the red wines and chenin blanc for the white. Pinotage is a variety developed in South Africa. The chenin blanc is sometimes known as steen.

Nooldeberg
Pinotage
Chenin Blanc

Australia

Vine cuttings and grape seeds reached Australia in 1788 with the first settlers. They were planted in humid, sub-tropical conditions near Sydney, and failed to produce any wine. In the 1830s the efforts of a young Scot named James Busby met with greater success and today Australia produces large quantities of impressive light wine, as well as dessert wines from botrytis affected grapes, and liqueur wines.

There has been an enormous expansion in wine production and consumption since the war. The wine-producing regions are near the cities of Sydney, Melbourne, Adelaide and Perth. The central and northern parts of Australia have an unsuitable climate.

The Barossa valley in South Australia, where good red wines are produced from the shiraz grape.

Australian states where wine is made are:

> **New South Wales**, where James Busby planted the first successful vineyard in the Hunter river valley.

> **Victoria**

> **South Australia**, which includes the Barossa valley and the Coonawarra district.

> **Western Australia**

Most Australian red wines are made from **cabernet sauvignon** and **shiraz**, either separately or as a blend. They tend to be full bodied, with rich fruit and only moderate tannin.

White wines from the **chardonnay** have been particularly successful, especially when oak aged. Other varieties used include **semillon** and **riesling** (rhine riesling).

New Zealand

New Zealand has only recently become a wine maker of any significance.

Most of the wine at present is grown in North Island, around Auckland, but much development is taking place now in South Island, particularly around Marlborough.

The temperate climate and good rainfall make New Zealand an excellent producer of varietal white wines. Grape varieties include chardonnay, gewurztraminer and sauvignon blanc.

Good red wines are also made from the cabernet sauvignon and pinot noir.

South America

Brazil, Argentina and Chile all make wine. Production is very considerable but only Chile currently has a real presence in the UK market.

Argentina

Though a large producer, Argentina produces wine of moderate quality. In the late 1970's, Argentinian wine producers started an export drive into Europe. Trade with Britain suffered following the 1982 Falklands conflict.

4th largest producer in the world.

Brazil

Most of Brazil is climatically unsuited for wine production. However, in southern Brazil, European immigrants started making wine with varieties from home. Almost none is exported to Britain.

Chile

Good red wines are produced, mainly from the cabernet sauvignon and merlot varieties. *3000 × @ 85*

North America

The earliest settlers in North America attempted to make wine from the native grapes. The results were not to their taste. Constant efforts were made to establish European *vinifera* vines on the east coast states, but they all failed. Eventually vitis vinifera was successfully planted on the west coast in California.

Prohibition (1919 - 1933), which forbade the sale of alcohol, undermined a healthy industry but since 1960 there has been an enormous development, mainly in California.

California

At present this is the most important wine producing region. The vineyards lie in the areas near the coast to the north and south of San Francisco. They are protected from excessive summer heat by frequent fog in the area. Major districts include the Napa and Sonoma Valleys.

Napa Valley

Grape Varieties

Most California wine exported to Britain is made from noble European varieties, especially the **cabernet sauvignon** for reds and the **chardonnay** and **sauvignon blanc** for whites. A red variety particular to California is the **zinfandel**, which produces full-bodied wines with rich fruit flavours.

California is an area of constant experimentation and innovation. The University of California Davis is one of the foremost centres in the world for the study of viticulture and vinification.

North Western States

Another area now making fine wines from noble grape varieties is the group of states comprising Idaho, Oregon and Washington. These states have a much cooler climate, and some fine wines are being produced.

They have a great potential for the future.

Chapter 8
Champagne and Sparkling Wines

The only difference between a still and a sparkling wine is the presence of bubbles when the wine is poured into the glass. These bubbles are created by trapping carbon dioxide (CO_2) in the wine.

There are four ways of putting the sparkle into wine:

> Traditional method (Méthode Champenoise)
> Tank method
> Transfer method
> Injection method

The first three use the process of fermentation (yeast acting on sugar to create alcohol and CO_2) to create the CO_2 in the wine. The fourth method injects the CO_2 from an external source.

Methods of Production

alternative phrase (Méthode Traditional)

Traditional Method (Méthode Champenoise) *only allowed to apply to region of champagne from 1994*

This describes a method developed in the Champagne region of northern France, whereby the sparkle is created in the same bottle in which the wine is sold. Although it is used in many other parts of the world, the European Commission has decreed, that as from 1994 the term 'Champagne Method' (Méthode Champenoise) may not be applied to any wine from outside the Champagne region.

A second fermentation is created by adding yeast and sugar to dry wine, which is then bottled. The second fermentation takes place within the bottle, leaving a sediment, which is subsequently removed. The removal process takes place in two stages called **remuage** and **dégorgement.**

The bottles of wine are then topped up with a mixture of similar wine and sugar syrup called the **liqueur d'expédition.** This may be sweetened with a measure of sugar, called the **dosage**. The dosage gives the final degree of sweetness to the wine.

A full descrpition of the method is given later in this chapter.

Tank Method

This is also known as **cuve close**, or **Charmat**. The method was first used by Eugène Charmat in Bordeaux in 1909.

Cuve close means closed tank. When wine is made by this method, second fermentation takes place in a sealed tank. The wine is then filtered from the sediment under pressure, receives the liqueur d'expédition and is bottled.

The tank method is a faster, much less expensive method than bottle fermentation. The wine is made and handled in bulk, and the complicated remuage and dégorgement processes are eliminated.

It is used to make bulk sparkling wine, particularly in Germany. However, the sparkle is rarely of such fine quality as in the traditional method, and so this method is forbidden for Appellation Contrôlée wines in France.

In Italy, however, asti spumante is made by a unique form of the tank method, using one fermentation only which is stopped at about 8 percent alcohol, leaving naturally sweet wine.

Transfer Method

This is also known as transvasement. It may be described as a compromise between the traditional and tank methods.

Second fermentation takes place in the bottle. After maturation, instead of the lengthy process of remuage and dégorgement, the bottles are chilled and disgorged into a pressurized tank. The sediment is filtered out and the liqueur d'expédition added. The wine is then rebottled, still under pressure.

This method gives a good sparkle which lasts quite well and wines made in this way may be found in Germany and the USA.

Injection Method

In this method the CO_2 is forced into a chilled, still wine under pressure. The French refer to this as 'pompe bicyclette', and it is a cheap, fast method of putting bubbles into wine. The bubbles are large and the sparkle fades almost at once when the wine is poured.

crémant - cream

France

Champagne	-	Champagne
The Loire	-	Sparkling Saumur AC, Crémant de Loire AC and sparkling Vouvray AC
Alsace	-	Crémant d'Alsace AC
Burgundy	-	Crémant de Bourgogne AC
The Midi	-	Blanquette de Limoux AC

All French sparkling wine with AC status MUST be made by the traditional method.

Spain

The main source is Penedés in Cataluña, with its production centred on the town of San Sadurni de Noya. **Cava** is the Spanish term for wine made sparkling by the traditional method. Its regions of production are defined.

Italy

Asti spumante is the major Italian DOC sparkling wine. It is a sparkling dessert wine made from the muscat grape grown in the vineyards around the town of Asti in Piemonte. It is made by a version of the tank method (see page 84).

Germany

Sparkling wine made in Germany is known as **Sekt**. The Germans are the largest consumers of sparkling wine per head of population in the world. Most Sekt is made by the tank method, although transfer and traditional method wines may be found.

New World

USA	California produces sparkling wine, the majority of which is made by the traditional method, although transfer method wines are found.
Australia	Most areas make sparkling wines.

The statue of Dom Perignon at Moët et Chandon, Epernay

Before the latter part of the 17th century, the much admired wines of Champagne had been still. In 1650, the Abbey of Hautvillers appointed a new cellarmaster. His name was Pierre Perignon.

Dom Perignon appears to have been the first person to exploit the idea of trapping the gas of fermentation in a wine, thereby creating a sparkle. He was also the first person to develop the blending system still used today, whereby the wines from different areas in Champagne, and made from the different grape varieties, are blended together.

Dom Perignon was assisted in the development of sparkling wine by two other factors. For the first time it was possible to obtain glass bottles strong enough to withstand the pressure. It was also possible to seal the bottles completely by using tighter corks (later to be wired) so that the gas could not escape. It appears that he had created the first fully sparkling wine by 1690, although its growth in popularity was not to start until about 30 years later.

Dom Perignon, however, had no method for clearing the sediment from the bottle. The system of remuage and dégorgement was developed in the early 19th century by the widow Clicquot (Veuve Clicquot) thus completing the system that is still used today.

There are many sparkling wines made by the same method as Champagne, and sometimes from the same grape varieties.

There is, however only one true *Champagne*.

Champagne cellars are hewn out of the chalk sub-soil. Here the bottles are resting in their pupîtres (see page 89).

Geographical Position

The region of Champagne lies in northern France about 80 miles north east of Paris, between latitudes 49 - 50° N.

Climate

The climate is northerly continental with warm summers but often bitterly cold winters. Over the year the temperature averages 10° C which is just sufficient to ripen the grape.

This climate is called MARGINAL.

Because of the difficulty in ripening all the varieties sufficiently, in some years the wines are very light in flavour. For this reason all champagne houses make a consistent non vintage wine by blending between vintages. Vintage champagnes are only made in the very best years.

Soil

The soil is a form of chalk covered by a thin layer of rich topsoil.

Grape Varieties

Three important grape varieties are grown:

> **pinot noir**
> **pinot meunier** } Red
> **chardonnay**

Main Vineyard Districts

Vine varieties are planted across the Champagne districts as follows:

Montagne de Reims	-	pinot noir
Vallée de la Marne	-	pinot noir/pinot meunier
Côte des Blancs	-	chardonnay

(Blanc de Blanc from white grapes)

The Champagne Method

[handwritten: i Pressing ii) First Fermentation]

After the harvest a long cool fermentation takes place in the normal way, leaving a still, dry wine. To turn this still wine into champagne, the following sequence of processes is used.

[handwritten: iii)]

1.   Assemblage

The still wines are blended together, usually in the spring following the vintage. The object of the blending is to produce a style of wine which is consistent from year to year. Each champagne maker has his own particular style which does not vary.

2.   Tirage

A mixture (liqueur de tirage) of cane sugar syrup and yeast is added to the blended wine, which is then bottled and closed with either a crown cap (most often) or a cork and wire. The bottles are then stacked on their sides (sur lattes) in cool, dark cellars.

Sparkling wine enclosures from left: a crown cap enclosure for bottle fermentation; a cork prior to the corking process; two corks removed from bottles. The cork on the far right has not retained its elasticity and may have failed to keep an airtight seal.

3.   Second fermentation

The second fermentation then takes place over a long period at a low temperature. When it is complete, the pressure created by the gas in the bottle is about six atmospheres (90 psi). At this point the bottles may be left for some time to age.

4.   Remuage

The second fermentation has created sediment in the bottles which must be removed.

Remuage, sometimes known as 'riddling' in English, is the method used to move the sediment towards the neck of the bottle, prior to its removal.

A remueur at work

The bottles are placed in specially designed racks (called pupîtres) with the neck slightly downwards. They are then turned and the tilt of the bottle gradually increased.

Over a period of up to two months, the sediment slowly moves into the neck of the bottle.

Mechanical remuage - the bottles are tilted and twisted in large metal cages.

5.   Ageing

The ageing process is continued. By law the total period of ageing must be a minimum of one year for non-vintage wines and three years minimum for vintage wines. The wines will gain aroma and flavour as a result.

6.   Dégorgement

This is the removal of the lees now collected in the neck of the bottle. It is done by passing the neck through a freezing solution, which creates a small plug of ice. On removal of the crown cap, this block of ice holding the sediment is forced out by the pressure of the gas.

Where a cork and wire are used for the second fermentation, dégorgement is carried out by hand, not machine.

Dégorgement by freezing. As the bottles move along a conveyor, an ice plug containing the sediment may be seen in the neck.

7.   Liqueur d'expédition

The bottle is then topped up with wine to which some cane sugar has been added. This *dosage* varies depending on the degree of sweetness required in the final wine. The bottle is then given a resting period for the dosage to marry with the original wine.

This sequence of processes (the traditional method) is considered the best way of making sparkling wine. It originated in the Champagne district and produces the finest bubbles which last the longest.

The Uniqueness of Champagne

It is believed that the soil, which is not found in any other wine region of the world, together with the highly marginal climate, the grape varieties and the care taken in the method of production account for the uniqueness of champagne.

The Legal Protection of Champagne

Champagne is a protected name. Within the European Community only sparkling wine from the Champagne region and made by the Champagne method may bear the name CHAMPAGNE. The name itself is the appellation even though 'AC' does not normally appear on the label.

From 1994, European regulations will forbid the use of the term 'methóde champenoise' or 'Champagne method' to describe any wine except champagne itself (see page 83).

Chapter 9
Liqueur Wines

A liqueur wine has a higher alcohol level than a light wine. This difference is usually the result of fortifying a light wine by the addition of spirit, generally local grape brandy.

Before Louis Pasteur did his work on yeasts and bacteria, wine makers in some hot climates had discovered that adding spirit would preserve wine.

The level of alcohol in a light wine is between 5.5% and 15% by volume. A liqueur wine is between 15% and 22%.

The most important liqueur wines are:

| Sherry | Port | Madeira | Vermouth |

Methods of Production

There are two main methods of making liqueur wine.

The sherry method

The must is fermented out, leaving a dry wine. The spirit is then added. If the final style of wine is other than dry, sweetening is added before bottling.

The port method

The must is only partly fermented, and the process is stopped by the addition of sufficient spirit to prevent the yeast working. The remaining unfermented grape sugar produces a sweet wine.

Sherry

Sherry is a wine made in south west Spain, around the town of Jerez de la Frontera, near Cadiz. The name 'Sherry' is protected by law and may only apply to the wine of Jerez.

Butts of sherry in a bodega, or warehouse

Climate

Jerez has hot, very dry summers, with mild winters. Rain falls between October and March.

Soil

There are three soil types.

Albariza is rich in chalk and is the best soil for sherry production (see page 17).

Barro and **Arena** are rich in clay and sand respectively. Many of the grapes harvested from vines grown on these soils, are used to contribute sweetness and colour to the medium and sweet styles of sherry (see page 95).

Grapes

Two main white grape varieties are grown.

Palomino   This, the most important grape, produces the base for sherry when grown on albariza soil (see above).

Pedro ximenez This grape variety makes the best sweetening wines and is usually referred to simply as PX.

Production of the Base Wine

After the grapes are crushed and pressed, the must is fermented to dryness. The wine is lightly fortified and stored in sherry casks, which are called **butts**. Early the following year the butts of wine undergo a classification.

Classification

Some butts of wine will have developed into a light, delicate style. These will be classified as **fino**, and the lighter styles of sherry which are called fino, manzanilla and amontillado, will develop from these butts. After this classification these butts will be only lightly fortified to encourage the development of **flor**.

Flor is unique to Jerez and grows on the surface of the wine. It looks like a whitish film, and is a type of yeast.

It is the presence of flor that produces the very distinctive, dry, 'yeasty' nose and flavour of light dry sherries.

Flor yeast in a butt of fino sherry

The other butts, developing into richer, heavier wines, will be classified as **oloroso**. These wines will produce the nuttier styles of sherry, such as oloroso and dark cream sherries. These styles do not require flor, and so, after this classification the wine is more heavily fortified to the point where flor cannot develop.

Whether fino or oloroso is being produced, the butts are only part-filled (five sixths), thereby leaving a pocket of air above the wine.

In the case of fino, the flor assimilates the oxygen and works on the wine, producing the character of fino sherries.

Oloroso on the other hand, matures in direct contact with the air in the butt. This results in a gradual oxidation of the wine, which in turn produces richness, breadth of flavour and natural colour.

Maturation

Sherry develops and matures in butts in a system which is called the **solera system**.

This system provides a means of adding younger wine to older wine so that the blend is consistent. This ensures that the taste of any chosen sherry never varies.

A solera system consists of a large number of butts, divided into groups known as scales. Each successive scale contains progressively older wine. Wine for shipment is drawn from the group containing the oldest wine. These butts are then replenished with younger wine from the next group of butts. These butts are themselves refilled with yet younger wine and so on throughout the system.

When a transfer of wine takes place, no more than a third of the contents of a butt is removed at any one time. This restriction ensures continuity of style.

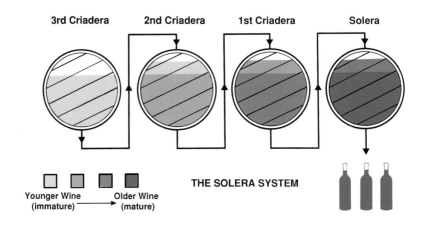

THE SOLERA SYSTEM

The solera system is divided into 3 parts.

1. Añada — wines of a year which develop different characteristics. As these wines are sufficiently matured, they are moved to the...—

2. Criadera — or nursery, where wines of similar character begin their maturation, being gradually blended from younger into older wines, the oldest of which is the...————

3. Solera — Finally, the wine moves into the solera itself until it is drawn off for shipment.

Styles of Sherry

From the fino classification

Fino — pale coloured, dry and drunk cold as an aperitif.

Manzanilla — fino wines matured in the small coastal town of Sanlúcar de Barrameda. It is the lightest and driest of sherries.

Amontillado — (a) older finos with a slightly richer, nuttier character, but dry.

— (b) commercial styles made sweeter and richer by the addition of oloroso and PX to fino sherry.

Pale cream — these are fino sherries with a light-coloured sweetening added.

From the oloroso classification

Oloroso — (a) classic, heavy, nutty, dry wines.

— (b) sweet oloroso, rich, sweetened and coloured.

Brown/Cream — rich, sweet styles, particularly popular in northern countries. These very popular, commercial styles are made by blending with sweet wines. Colour is adjusted by adding grape juice which has been heated until very dark in colour.

The Legal Protection of Sherry

Under UK law, some countries which have traditionally made this style of liqueur wine may still use the term 'sherry'. However, the name of the country of origin must appear immediately before the word sherry.

These wines are - **British Sherry**
Cyprus Sherry
Irish Sherry

Other countries produce wines of a similar style but they cannot be called sherry in the European Community.

Port

The wines of Porto, or Oporto, have been shipped to the UK for at least four centuries. They became increasingly important after the Methuen Treaty between Britain and Portugal in 1703. Many of the major port companies were founded by English and Scottish families who still run them today.

Port is wine of the Upper Douro which has been fortified by the addition of grape brandy.

As far as the UK is concerned, the name 'Port' is protected by the Anglo-Portuguese Trade Treaties of 1914 and 1916. Port wine may only come from Portugal and nowhere else.

Geographical Location

The Upper Douro starts 45 miles inland from the coast at the city of Oporto and stretches east to the Spanish border. The main centres are Pinhão and Regua.

Only about a third of the wine made here becomes port. The remainder is light wine.

Climate

The climate is one of great extremes. The summers are intensely hot, while the winters are very cold. A great deal of rain falls between January and April.

Soil

The soil is very poor and rocky. It is composed of broken down **schist,** a crumbly rock. The vineyards are laid out in narrow terraces on very steep slopes.

Schist

Grape Varieties

A significant number of red varieties are permitted.

A few white grapes are grown to make white port.

Vinification

The vintage normally takes place in late September. The grapes are pressed, either by foot in stone lagars (vats) or usually today by machine. Fermentation takes place, either in the lagar or in a closed vat known as an autovinificator.

When sufficient colour has been extracted from the skins and there is still a high proportion of unfermented grape sugar in the must, the wine is drawn from the skins and mixed with sufficient grape brandy to stop fermentation. This leaves a sweet wine.

The wine is stored in the quintas (wine farms) where it was made, and in the spring it is taken down to the warehouses (called lodges) usually in Vila Nova de Gaia, the town on the opposite side of the river from Oporto, and where the young port is matured.

During this maturation period, port is stored in casks called **pipes**, which hold approximately 600 litres each.

Types of Port

There are several types of port, the most prominent being:

Ruby port

This is a young port and is normally blended from wines of between 3 and 8 years old. It is a rich, ruby colour, very fruity and sweet. 'Vintage character' is a term used to describe a ruby port of superior quality.

Tawny port

A more elegant, mellow wine which has matured for eight years or more before being blended and bottled. During maturation it loses the intense sweetness and brilliant colour of the very young wines and becomes browner. Some tawny ports may be 20 or 30 years old.

Commercial tawny ports can be made by blending ruby and white ports together. These wines are usually sold for the same price as a ruby port.

White port

This wine is made from white grapes only, and may be medium sweet or medium dry. The latter style would be described on the label as 'dry'. It matures for two years only.

Vintage port

In a good year it will be possible to make vintage port. This is a red wine from a single year which is given only two years of cask ageing, followed by many years of maturation in bottle. An excellent quality port may result, but it will only be appreciated fully if the bottle is carefully decanted. The protracted period of bottle ageing, often lasting for decades, results in a sediment which can be considerable.

A vintage is declared in Portugal, by the port shippers who own, mature and ship the wine, only when they believe the wine to be of outstanding quality. The greatest years recently have been 1963, 1966, 1970, 1977, and 1985.

Late bottled vintage port (LBV)

This is port of a single year only, but one which the shipper did not think fine enough for declaration as a vintage port. LBV is bottled between the 4th and 6th year after the harvest. It usually does not need decanting.

Madeira

Madeira is the other great liqueur wine of Portugal and is made on the island of the same name.

Geographical Location

Madeira is a small island in the Atlantic Ocean, 350 miles from the coast of Morocco.

Climate

Madeira is sub-tropical with a warm, temperate climate the whole year round. The centre of the island is frequently very cloudy, and there is heavy rainfall. Nonetheless, irrigation is necessary on the coastal terraces, during dry periods.

The island of Madeira. Terraced vineyards are visible to the right.

Soil

The island is very mountainous with fertile, volcanic soil. The vines grow on terraced vineyards round the coast at high altitudes. The lower terraces now grow bananas as a main crop.

Grape Varieties

There are four major styles of madeira wine, named after the grape varieties traditionally used:

Sercial	-	the driest of the madeira styles
Verdelho	-	medium dry and fairly light
Bual	-	rich and medium sweet
Malmsey	-	rich and very sweet

Vinification

Much madeira today is made by the sherry system, in which sweeter styles are produced by blending, as opposed to the port method of arrested fermentation.

After the must has been fully fermented, it is racked and then fortified. In the past, the island grew much sugar cane, and the fortification was done with cane sugar spirit. Today, grape spirit is used and has to be imported from Portugal.

The new wine is put through a process unique to madeira called **estufagem**. Historically, in the days of sailing ships, casks of madeira wine were shipped as 'ballast'. During the slow voyage around the world to the Indies and back, the wine was gradually warmed up and then cooled. This was found to mellow and mature the wine and give it a cooked character of its own.

When these voyages were no longer necessary, they were replaced by the estufa system. The estufa is a hot store where the wines are slowly heated to a temperature of 40 - 50° C, held at this temperature for 3 to 6 months, and then slowly cooled. It is this heating which gives the traditional 'burnt' flavour to the wines.

After estufagem the wines are rested for a year to 18 months, before being blended in a solera system and bottled.

Vermouth

Most vermouths are made in the south of France and northern Italy.

Vermouth is a term derived from the German word 'Wermut', their name for the wormwood shrub whose flowers are used in its manufacturing process.

Vermouths are made from four basic ingredients:

1. A base wine which is high in alcohol.

2. Sugar syrup, or alternatively mistelle, which is fortified, unfermented grape juice.

3. Spirit.

4. Herbs, spices and plants, such as wormwood, camomile, cloves, cinnamon and vanilla.

Method

The herbs and flavourings are macerated in spirit and then this flavoured alcohol is blended into the base wine which has been sweetened. The blend is then rested so that the flavours marry together. The resulting drink is then fined, refrigerated and pasteurised to ensure stability.

Vermouth is made in the following styles:

White:	dry or sweet
Red:	sweet

There is one vermouth made in France which has its own AC. This is chambéry, made in the mountains of Savoie, and flavoured with alpine herbs. 'Chambéry fraises' will be flavoured with wild strawberries.

Other Liqueur Wines

Marsala DOC

This is the famous liqueur wine of Sicily developed by two Englishmen, Woodhouse and Smith, who in 1773 added some sweet wine and a little brandy to the local white wine.

Marsala is made from grapes grown on chalky soil around the port of Marsala. Two other elements are added to the base wine, grape brandy and 'vino cotto'. Vino cotto is produced by boiling down unfermented grape juice until it is thick and brown.

Main Styles

Marsala fine may be dry or sweet. It is aged for four months only.

Marsala superiore spends two years in cask.

Marsala vergine is lighter in style, having no vino cotto added, and it is aged by a solera system.

Many marsalas are flavoured, such as all'uovo with egg and crema mandorla, which has an almond taste. These flavoured marsalas are known as marsala speciale.

Vins Doux Naturels

These are specialities of southern France and are made by the port method of stopping fermentation to leave a sweet liqueur wine.

The grape varieties used are:

> muscat for the white wines.
> grenache for the red wines.

A particular style is made by leaving them out in the open for two winters and a summer. This produces a curious flavour called 'rancio'.

All vins doux naturels are appellation contrôlée wines. The most famous red wines are Rasteau AC and Banyuls AC. The muscat wines add the name of the district of production to the grape name, for example: muscat de beaumes de venise from the Rhône and muscat de rivesaltes from Languedoc-Rousillon.

Other liqueur wines are:

Malaga - sometimes called 'mountain wine', made in Spain.

Commandaria - from Cyprus.

Moscatel de Setúbal - made from muscat grapes grown in the peninsula of Setúbal in Portugal.

Montilla - only part of its production being fortified (see page 72).

Chapter 10
Beer

Basic Facts

The essential ingredient of beer is **malted barley**.When barley is 'malted', its starch is converted to sugar. During brewing, this sugar is extracted from the malt with water. It is then fermented by yeast into alcohol.

The flower of the **hop** plant is used to flavour the brew, giving it bitterness and aroma.

Production and Consumption

Beer is brewed all over the world. In 1987, most countries drank more beer than wine; the only notable exceptions were France, Italy, Portugal and Greece.

Considering its size, it is hardly surprising that the USA is the world's largest brewing nation. However, in terms of consumption per head, the USA lags behind the countries of northern and central Europe.

Top beer consumers are Austria, Belgium, the UK, Czechoslovakia, Denmark, East Germany, the Irish Republic, Luxembourg and West Germany. In northern Europe's cool climate, it has always been easier to grow barley for beer than to ripen grapes for wine.

Beer in the UK

Beer comes in many types;   traditional to the UK are bitter, mild, pale ale, light ale, brown ale, stout and barley wine.

During this century a type of beer known as **lager** has been imported to the UK from Europe. Increasingly popular since the 1960's, it is now widely brewed in the UK.

The type of lager that has made enormous inroads into the beer market both here and all over the world, is based on one made since the 17th century in Pilsen in Bohemia (now in Czechoslovakia). To mark this light, delicately aromatic style the beer is often given the description **Pils** or **Pilsner.**

A different consumer boom is the one stimulated by the organisation **CAMRA,** the Campaign for Real Ale.

CAMRA was set up in 1971. A basic theme of the campaign is that British beer or "ale" is a natural product and need not be stabilised by pasteurisation or filtration, nor altered by the injection of carbon dioxide gas. Most breweries now recognise the need to supply beer in its natural state. **Real ale** is very much a consumer issue, although it does not have a legal definition.

As the demand for beer to drink at home increases, a wider range of 'take-home' products and packages has been developed. Beer is packaged in bottles of glass or plastic, cans and large plastic containers with a tap dispenser.

A significant marketing trend in recent years has been the identification of 'special' or 'premium' beers, which can command significantly higher prices than the more usual categories.

A Brief History

The word 'beer' probably originates from the Anglo-Saxon **baere**, which means barley. The drink has its origins at least as far back as 5,000 years ago. Stone carvings from that time show that the ancient Egyptians made and drank a grain brew known as 'hek'.

Three thousand years later, when the Romans introduced winemaking into northern Europe, they noted the Gallic and Saxon habit of beer drinking. It was observed at the time that the Britons were accustomed to gathering in their ale-houses to govern and adjudicate.

It is not exactly clear how the beer was made until the Middle Ages, except that it was generally a sweet drink.

A kegging plant. In the foreground kegs are being filled, while in the background others are being sterilized with steam.

A variety of herbs was also used to flavour it. The establishment in Europe of hops as the dominant flavouring, reached England in the 15th century, resulting in modern beer.

104

The next four centuries saw the development in Europe of lager beer which requires different methods of brewing (see yeast, page 107).

Barley

Barley is important to beer for three main reasons:

It is composed of 80% starch, which once converted, is the primary source of fermentable sugar.

Barley   **After germination (see page 109)**

Barley is a grain which contains substantial amounts of an enzyme called **diastase**. Diastase is indispensable to the brewing process because it converts starch, which is unfermentable, into sugar, which is fermentable.

In its malted form, barley provides a rich flavour.

Other Grains

Grains such as maize, wheat or rice, used in conjunction with malted barley, are a useful and often economical, secondary source of sugar. These ingredients are known as **adjuncts.**

However, the starch of these grains can only be converted to sugar when the diastase of barley is present.

Sugar

As with wine, sugar is sometimes added before fermentation to increase the potential alcohol. In some cases it is also used to sweeten beer after fermentation. For example, sweet stout is sweetened with lactose (milk sugar).

The use of sugar in brewing was officially recognised in Britain by an Act of Parliament in 1847. Some European countries forbid the use of either sugar or adjuncts in their brews. Germany is the most important one.

Hops

Hops contribute flavour only and do not affect sugar or alcohol.

The botanical name of the hop plant is '*humulus lupulus*', and it is grown throughout the world but especially in Germany, Czechoslovakia, southern England and North America. The flower of the female hop plant is the part used to flavour beer. In Britain the hop is fertilised and therefore contains seeds; seeded hops impart more bitterness, a characteristic for which British beer is noted.

Hops provide three elements in the taste and character of beer:

Aroma
Various oils provide the hop with an aroma which, in good beers, can be clearly detected on the nose. The most aromatic hops are often described as flowery.

Bitterness
Balances the richness of the malt.

Tannin

Hops

The lightly tannic nature of beer is easily overlooked, but it is vital to the feel and taste of many brews.

Historically, many herbs have been used to flavour grain beverages. Widespread use of hops was established during the 9th century in Europe. The introduction of the hop to England in the 15th century provoked considerable controversy. Until then the barley brew in England was unhopped, usually sweet, and known as **ale**.

For the next hundred years ale (unhopped) versus beer (hopped) was the subject of fierce debate in the taverns. Beer finally carried the day and the term ale gradually fell into disuse. In the latter half of the 20th century, with the growth in demand for continental styles of lager beer, 'ale' has resurfaced as a term for traditional British beers.

Important types of hops include **Goldings** and **Fuggles**; two British varieties which provide a good balance of bitterness and aroma.

Most continental beer styles depend on less bitter, highly aromatic varieties. The classic example is the **Saaz** hop originally cultivated in Bohemia.

Water

Hard water, rich in minerals, is excellent for bitters. Soft water, found in mountainous regions such as the Bavarian Alps, is ideal for the lager style of beer.

Many breweries are located to exploit the natural water of the area. For example, several breweries are sited on the river Trent at Burton-on-Trent, in the Midlands.

In most cases however, a brewer cannot be certain of a constant supply of natural water which has an ideal mineral balance. It is normal therefore to adjust the mineral content in the brewery. Whether or not this adjustment has been done, the water which is used in the brew is known as **liquor**.

Yeast

Yeast converts the sugar into alcohol and carbon dioxide.

There are two main types of yeast, suited to different conditions and producing different styles of beer.

Saccharomyces cerevisiae

For centuries, the yeast used for brewing was one similar to bakers' yeast. It operated best at around room temperature and would float to the surface of the brew during fermentation.

Brewery workers preparing to take a sample of fermenting beer from below the yeast crop

This yeast is still used, particularly in Britain. The thick foamy layer of yeast which forms on the liquid's surface is known as a **yeast crop**. It forms a barrier, preventing invasion of the brew by airborne wild yeasts and bacteria.

Saccharomyces carlsbergensis

In Bavaria during the early 15th century, it was discovered that if beer was kept at low temperatures during production, it was less likely to go sour. The whole process was slower at a low temperature, including the stage of maturation of the fermented brew. The beer was allowed to mature slowly in large stores known as **lagers**. The delicately flavoured beer that resulted became known as **lager beer**. It was best drunk cool.

The species of yeast which reproduced and survived best under these conditions was one which did not float, rather it was **bottom-fermenting.**

Its scientific name was given by the Carlsberg brewery which first cultivated the yeast as a pure strain.

With the yeast on the bottom of the fermenting vessel, the liquid is not protected from the air and for this reason the process takes place in a closed fermenter.

Brewing

There are five processes involved in the brewing of beer:

1. Conversion

The unfermentable starch in the grain is converted into fermentable sugar.

2. Extraction

The malt is soaked in order to bring the sugars into solution.

3. Flavouring

The sweet solution is flavoured with hops.

4. Fermentation

The sugar is converted into alcohol by the action of yeast.

5. Conditioning

The beer is made ready for drinking.

Conversion

After harvesting, the barley grain is **steeped,** (soaked) in water. This stimulates germination.

Then the excess water is drained away and the germinating barley is kept under carefully controlled conditions of warmth and moisture. As germination proceeds the diastase begins the conversion of starch into sugar.

At a certain point, germination is ended by drying the grain by controlled heat in a kiln. This produces what is known as **malted barley** or **malt**.

There are different types of malted barley which depend on the amount of heat applied during the kilning. The basis of all brews is known as **pale malt**. This has received only a light roasting and produces the most fermentable sugar.

Higher degrees of heating caramelise (burn), the sugars in the grain to a greater or lesser extent. This reduces the amount of fermentable sugar available but increases the flavour and the colour of the eventual beer.

Beer may be given a darker colour and a richer flavour by including with the malt a certain proportion of unmalted barley which has been highly roasted and has had its starch caramelised by heat.

There are four types of malt:

Pale malt	-	is lightly roasted and produces the maximum amount of fermentable sugar. It is the basis of all beer.
Lager malt	-	is used for lagers. It is a very lightly roasted pale malt, light in colour but giving slightly less sugar than normal pale malts.
Crystal malt	-	is golden brown in colour as a result of a medium roasting. Crystal malt provides a fuller flavour and colour when added to beers, even in small proportions.
Black or Chocolate malt	-	has had its sugars caramelised. A very small amount will result in black-coloured beer with a cocoa or chocolate flavour. These malts are used for stouts.

Extraction

To give access to sugars inside the grain, it is first crushed in a mill, producing a cracked malted barley which is known as **grist**. The grist, plus any other malted grains which are being used to supplement it, are soaked in water at a temperature of 65°C for a period of about 2 hours. This process is known as **mashing** and takes place in a **mash tun**. During this period the diastase completes the conversion of starch into sugar.

The soaking releases the sugar into solution, and the sugary, sweet solution called **wort** (pronounced 'wert') can be run off.

Extraction is most efficient if the barley grains which remain in the mash tun are then sprayed with water of the same temperature as was used for soaking. This is known as **sparging**, and rinses out the remaining sugar. This liquid is added to the wort.

A mash tun

Flavouring

The wort is now transferred to a vessel known as a **copper** and is boiled for one to two hours. It is during this time that the hops are added and impart their characteristic bitterness and aroma to the wort.

If sugar is to be used to increase the potential alcohol, it will also be added at this stage.

Before fermentation can begin, the sweet liquid, now known as **hopped wort** has to be cooled to a temperature of 20°C.

It is at this stage that the wort is assessed by HM Customs & Excise officials for its potential alcohol.

Fermentation

The yeast is 'pitched' into the wort at a temperature of around 20° C. Within hours it becomes active and fermentation normally lasts up to a week. In the case of top-fermenting yeasts the first three or four days can take place in an open container.

After the end of fermentation, a common practice is to add a small amount of hops to the brew. this is known as **dry hopping**. In this way some of the flavours which were destroyed at the boiling stage, are now reintroduced.

Conditioning

When fermentation is complete, the new beer needs to be **conditioned**. This involves both clarification and the encouragement of a light CO_2 sparkle.

Each of these can happen naturally.

Settling of contents plus racking will clarify beer, and enough yeast will remain to promote a continued slight fermentation, creating a small sparkle. This may be assisted by the addition of a small amount of sugar, a process known as **priming**. Such beers are described as 'naturally conditioned' and the term may apply whether the beer is bottled or in cask. Casks may be wooden or metal.

The conditioning room in a modern brewery

Cask conditioned beer has a limited life. It is only good for a few days once the cask has been broached.

To promote stability, instead of leaving clarification and conditioning to nature, the former may be achieved by fining and filtration and the latter by CO_2 injection.

A keg is a pressurised metal cask which can be left on ullage without risk of the beer spoiling. The beer is dispensed from it under CO_2 pressure, which results in a greater gas content than in cask conditioned beers.

'Real ale' is a term used by supporters of natural conditioning to describe beers made by that method.

THE BREWING PROCESS

RAW MATERIALS	PREPARATION	BREWING	BY-PRODUCTS

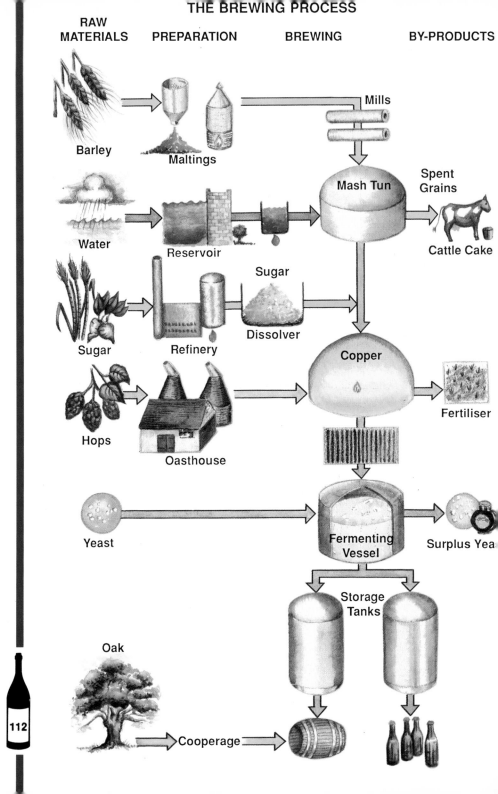

Barley

Maltings

Mills

Mash Tun

Spent Grains

Water

Reservoir

Cattle Cake

Sugar

Refinery

Sugar

Dissolver

Copper

Hops

Oasthouse

Fertiliser

Yeast

Fermenting Vessel

Surplus Yeast

Storage Tanks

Oak

Cooperage

Main Types of Beer

Lager   A bottom-fermented brew.

Most lagers from the UK, USA and Australia are imitations of the Pilsner style; light-golden in colour with a light-flavoured, hoppy style. Alcohol is usually low at about 3% alcohol. 'Premium' lagers, many imported in bottle from Europe, are stronger, at around 5 or 6% alcohol.

Bitter   The classic British draught beer. Its name is derived from the use of bitter English hops. It is full in flavour and usually amber in colour. Strength varies between 3% and 5% alcohol.

Traditionally, when this style of beer is bottled, it is known either as pale ale or light ale, at higher or lower strengths respectively.

Stout   Stouts are beers which are richly flavoured and black in colour through the introduction of highly roasted malt. Bitter stout is dry and highly hopped. Sweet stout is sweetened by the addition of lactose (milk sugar).

Other Types of Beer:

Mild   -   low in alcohol and lightly hopped

Brown ale -   medium sweet and well coloured

Strong ale - in a bitter style but with extra flavour and alcohol

Barley wine - a strong sweet beer with an alcohol level of up to 10% vol.

Cider Production

Apples
Press
fermat
Mature
(sweeten)
Bottle or can

Chapter 11
Cider and Perry

Cider and perry are long established alcoholic beverages. Each has been made since ancient times in Asia and in Britain and Western Europe since before the Romans arrived.

Specialised cider apples are cultivated in the south west of England, namely in Avon, Cornwall, Devon, Dorset, Gloucestershire, Hereford, Worcestershire and Somerset.

The eastern counties which produce cider from dessert and culinary apples, include Kent, Norfolk, Suffolk and Sussex. The end product is sometimes given the alternative spelling 'cyder'.

The alcoholic strengths of ciders and perries range between 4% and 8% vol. Anything above 8.5% is categorised as apple wine, and taxed at the same rate as British made wine.

Understandably, more cider and perry is consumed in the south of England, where it is produced. They are also to a large extent young persons' drinks. In 1987 over 60% of cider was drunk by people in the 18 to 24 age group.

Ingredients

Cider is made from apples and perry from pears, although each drink may include in its ingredients up to 25% of the other fruit. The methods of production are very similar.

The remainder of this chapter will refer to cider alone, making reference to perry only where appropriate.

Two varieties of apple being received by a cider producer

Cider apples

Grown in the western counties, cider apples are distinguished from culinary and dessert varieties by their greater bitterness, also by the flesh of the fruit which releases its juice more efficiently when pressed.

Different varieties of cider apple are selected for the degrees of bitterness and acidity which they impart when blended.

Sugar

Sugar may be added, either to enrich the juice prior to fermentation (see chaptalisation of wine on page 24), or to sweeten the cider after fermentation.

Carbon dioxide

Carbon dioxide is usually injected before bottling to provide a slight sparkle. In some cases it may be produced by promoting a second fermentation in tank.

Production

Harvesting

Apples are harvested from late September until well into October. Pears ripen a little earlier.

The modern picking process employs three types of machine harvester. First, a 'shaker' attaches its arm to the trunk of the apple tree and vibrates it to dislodge the fruit to the ground. Next, blowers or sweepers push the apples out from under the trees. Finally, 'gatherers' collect the fruit by flipping it off the ground, like the operation of the rotating brush of a household vacuum cleaner.

Selecting and Washing

At the mill, the apples are transported through water courses, where any rotten fruit will sink and be discarded. Good apples are then lifted and washed by water spray.

Milling

Whole apples are far too tough to release the juice when pressed, so they first have to be milled, by high speed steel blades, into a fine pulp.

Pressing

Traditionally, apple pulp is pressed by constructing a 'cheese'. This consists of pulp, wrapped in packets of coarse cloth, interposed with wooden boards. These layers are piled up and then great vertical pressure is applied to extract the juice, which runs between the boards and into a collecting trough.

Cheeses, pressed by hydraulic action, are still used widely in the cider industry. However, as they take a long time to construct, the major cider makers are placing increasing reliance on more automated methods. These include the squeezing of pulp between rollers.

A 'cider cheese' in production

Whichever method is used, a pressure greater than that normally employed for grape pressing, must be achieved. Cider pulp releases about 80% of its weight in juice.

Fermentation

Traditional wooden fermenting vats are being supplanted by the more readily maintained lined concrete or stainless steel vessels.

As with grape must, the juice is normally lightly sulphured to kill wild yeasts, then fermented with cultured yeasts.

Once fermentation has begun, the juice may be enriched by sugar or apple concentrate. This is similar to the chaptalisation of wine.

Fermentation lasts for about four weeks. Most ciders are fermented to dryness. Sugar or concentrate, added before bottling, produces sweeter styles.

Maturation

Cider, unlike most wines, needs only to mature for a few weeks before consumption. During this time it should to some degree 'fall bright', that is, throw a sediment and become clearer.

Preparation for Sale

Most commercial ciders are sold as clear in appearance and with a light sparkle. Clarity is achieved by fining or centrifuging, followed by filtration. The injection of a little carbon dioxide provides sparkle.

Sugar or apple concentrate may be used to produce a degree of sweetness. Most ciders are at least medium dry.

Cider may be packaged in bottles, cans or in pressurised barrels known as **kegs** (see page 112).

Types and Styles of Cider

For convenience, cider can be divided into four types:

Standard ciders

Standard ciders are normally between 4% and 6% alcohol, and are made lightly sparkling. The degree of sweetness varies between medium dry (often labelled 'dry') and medium sweet.

Sparkling ciders

Cider and perry may be made more fully sparkling by inducing a refermentation in a sealed tank, as in the 'tank' method for producing sparkling wine (see page 84).

Sparkling ciders and perries are made in England and also in Normandy, which has exported to the UK in recent years. Alcohol levels are similar to those of standard ciders, although Normandy ciders have a more distinctive apple flavour.

These ciders are often sold in wine-style bottles with a wired-on plastic 'cork'.

Farmhouse ciders or 'scrumpy'

These terms are used for the ciders which are in a literal sense less refined, and therefore regarded by some as more authentic.

They are typically still and dry, and are often strong in alcohol, levels of 6% to 8% being common. Being usually unfiltered, they may appear cloudy.

Other ciders

Low alcohol cider, at a level of less than 1.2%, fulfills an important demand for those who are looking for taste with a lesser influence of alcohol.

Premium quality ciders, sometimes labelled as 'special', are made from a selection of the best fruit and are usually at a higher level of alcohol (6% to 8% vol).

An example of premium quality cider is vintage cider, which uses the fruit of a single harvest year and shows some variation in style from year to year. It is currently produced in both England and Normandy.

Distillation: Key Facts

- Alcohol concentrated by heat
- Pot still vs Patent still
- colouring
- Breaking down — adding water after distillation

v. few spirits sold at maturation level
watered down to ~ 40%
Export strength usually 43%
gin 47.3%

Chapter 12
Spirits and Liqueurs

A spirit is the product of distillation, whatever the base raw material used.

A spirit for human consumption, referred to as a 'potable' or drinkable spirit, is made by distilling a lower strength alcoholic liquid. This alcoholic liquid must have been made by the fermentation of the sugar in fruit, vegetable or grain produce.

Two obvious examples are:

Brandy	-	distilled from wine
Whisky	-	distilled from a form of ale.

Background to Distillation

The distillation process was known to the ancient Chinese and Egyptians who used it to produce perfumes. Potable spirits were distilled by early Christian missionary monks who called them 'aqua vitae' or water of life.

Their taste was crude and so it was often disguised by other flavours, such as herbs, seeds and fruit.

By the 18th century, distillation had reached the point where cheap spirits were readily available. As there were no controls, many of these were rough and impure. To ensure that only safe, potable spirits were sold and to raise revenue, the Government began to license distilleries.

This policy is still the legal position in the UK today.

Principles of Distillation

The process of distillation takes place in a still and involves heating an alcoholic liquid until the alcohol vapourises. This vapour is then condensed to a liquid of a higher degree of alcohol.
Most spirits are sold at 40% vol, although some, especially liqueurs, are sold at lower or higher strengths.

Types of Still

There are two types of still:

Pot still

The pot still is made of copper and the neck is connected to a condenser which is surrounded by cold water.

Pot distillation is a single batch process and more than one distillation is required to produce a spirit of sufficient alcoholic strength.

The distillate is divided into three parts:

Pot stills in a malt whisky distillery

Heads (sometimes called 'foreshots') This part is of insufficient strength and is redistilled as part of a later batch.

Hearts (or 'spirit') This is the major part of the distillation, which produces the potable spirit.

Tails (or 'feints') This last part, like foreshots, is transferred to a later batch for redistillation.

The residue in the still, called 'spent lees', is run to waste.

Spirits, distilled in a pot still, will keep some of the character of the original alcoholic liquid, examples being **malt whisky** and **cognac.** They need to be matured in cask before being mellow enough to drink.

Patent still

Sometimes called the continuous or Coffey still. This still was invented in 1831 by an Irish customs officer, Aeneas Coffey.

It is a continuous process in which the spirit vapours are condensed at a greater strength than in the pot still.

The patent still produces a spirit of high alcoholic strength which consequently has less flavour and character than the spirit produced in a pot still.

Patent still spirits also require maturation.

A patent still is used for lightly flavoured spirits such as **white rum**, **grain whisky, gin** and **vodka**.

Raw Materials of Distillation

There are three major ingredients used for spirits:

> **Grain**, which produces whiskies, gin and vodka.

> **Fruit**, the source of brandies, calvados, kirsch, etc.

> **Vegetable**, the source of rums, arrack, schnapps and tequila.

Grain Spirits

Blended - malts & grains

Scotch whisky

Scotch whisky is defined in law as 'Spirits distilled from a mash of cereals, saccharified (starch converted to sugar) by the diastase of malt, fermented by yeast, distilled and matured in oak casks in Scotland for not less than three years.'

Whisky takes its name from the Gaelic words 'uisge beathe' which, like 'aqua vitae', means water of life.

Blending of malt with grain whisky was introduced in the nineteenth century, but it was only after a Royal Commission in 1909 that such blends could legally be called 'scotch whisky'.

Malt whisky is made exclusively from malted barley and distilled in pot stills.
more expensive than grain whiskey
The process has five main stages:

Malting • Mashing • Fermentation • Distillation • Maturation

Malting and mashing take place in exactly the same way as for beer (see page 110).

Blended: malt/grain
standard 30/70 All bms named
deluxe 40/60 namey blended
grain: Mixed Grain patent still

Scotch whiskey Key Facts
Distilled & Matured in Scotland
Malt : Grain : Blended
Malt : Malted Barley Pot still
— Highland: Lowland
Islay : Campbeltown

123

Most Malt whiskey goes to make blended

In the making of whisky, emphasis is placed on the character of the local spring water used during mashing.

Once the wort has been drawn off, it is cooled, passed to a fermentation vat called a washback and fermented with yeast to produce the 'wash', a liquid of low alcoholic strength.

The wash is then distilled twice in a pot still (in some distilleries - three times) before being put into cask for a maturation period of not less than 3 years. Scotch whisky must be matured in Scotland.

Grain whisky is made from a mixture of maize and malted barley, and then distilled in a patent still, producing a lighter flavoured spirit, used for blending, other spirit drinks or for industrial purposes.

Most scotch whisky is a blend of malt and grain whiskies. The 'premium' blends contain a higher percentage of older malt whiskies.

In recent years there has been a growing demand for malt whiskies from single distilleries.

Each distillery makes its own individual style of malt whisky.

Unchallenged by technology, the whisky blender's nose serves as a highly sensitive instrument.

Other whiskies

Whiskey (note the spelling) is produced in other countries, such as the USA, Canada and Ireland.

Irish whiskey is a pot still spirit based on malted barley and other cereals, distilled three times and matured in wood for three years.

Rye whisky is made in Canada and the USA (bourbon), from malted barley with rye or maize. Rye whisky is made by the patent still method.

Bourbon is the most famous of American whiskies. It originated in Bourbon County, Kentucky, but may now be made throughout the USA. Based on malted barley and rye, bourbon is matured for two years in new oak casks charred on the inside.

Fruit Spirits

Brandy is the oldest and most important of the fruit spirits. The name is probably a corruption of the term 'brandewijn' or burnt wine, since all brandy is distilled from wine.

Other fruit spirits include **calvados**, the apple brandy made in northern France, **slivovitz** made in Yugoslavia from plums, and **kirsch** in France from cherries. Alsace and Germany produce fruit spirits from soft fruit such as strawberries, raspberries and apricots.

Pre-eminent among brandies are two AC spirits, **cognac** and **armagnac**.

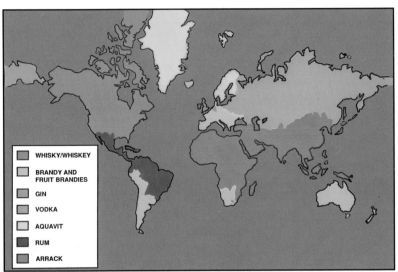

WHISKY/WHISKEY
BRANDY AND FRUIT BRANDIES
GIN
VODKA
AQUAVIT
RUM
ARRACK

Source of the world's main spirits

Cognac

from St Emilion Grape – Ugni Blanc (no connection to wine)

Cognac comes from the Charentes district of France, north of Bordeaux, and centred on the town of Cognac.

Same sort of wine as champagne

The climate is maritime and the best soil is chalk. The wine produced is light, fruity and highly acidic. It is distilled twice in pot stills.

from Limousin or Français Woods

The young brandy is put into (oak casks) and when mature it is blended. French law demands at least 2 years in oak before the cognac may be sold, but 3 years' oak maturation is required before it may be sold in the UK.

very special old Pale – 7-10 years decant

Styles include VSOP which must have longer maturation in cask. 'Fine Champagne' is the name for brandies blended between the two finest areas in Cognac, Grande Champagne and Petite Champagne.

Most have 3 quality steps   3 STAR/VS – Min of 2 years   decant brand s/b years in casks

125

Armagnac *fuller & earthier than Cognac*

South east and inland from Bordeaux is Gascony, home of the other AC grape brandy.

Being inland, Armagnac has a hotter climate, and here the finest soil is sand. After fermentation the wine is distilled. This may be done in the traditional local still, but often today in the Charentais pot still as is used for cognac. The brandy is matured in oak casks.

Of these two AC brandies, cognac is usually the lighter, having more obvious acidity and, perhaps, elegance.

The traditional, distinctive armagnac bottle

Armagnac tends to have a fuller flavour, and is often deeper in colour.

Calvados

In Normandy, between St. Malo and the Somme, the apple harvest is fermented into cider each autumn. The cider may then be distilled into calvados.

If the appellation is AC Calvados du Pays d'Auge, the pot still is used. Other calvados may be made by the patent still method.

A similar spirit may be made from a base of pears.

Vegetable Spirits

Vegetable based spirits include rum and vodka.

Rum

Rum is a spirit distilled from sugar cane.

It is made in:-

> The Caribbean • Indonesia • The Americas • Australia

Armagnac: Keyka
AC Brandy of Pyrenees
Picpoul
Pot still & Armagnac still
Pyrenean Oaky wood

90% of UK rum

The basis is molasses, the residue left when all usable sugar and syrup has been extracted from the sugar cane. The molasses is diluted with water and fermented.

Originally all rum was the product of a pot still, and had a very strong flavour.

Harvesting sugar cane - the raw material for rum

Today, most rums are blended from pot and continuous still spirits. White rums are the products of continuous stills.

The colour in dark rum comes from the addition of caramel.

Vodka

Vodka originated in the Baltic and Russia, where it was made from surplus agricultural crops, and was often flavoured. In the West, vodka is made from a basis of cane sugar spirit or grain spirit which has been highly rectified.

A rectified spirit is one that has been re-distilled to eliminate impurities and produce a very pure, high strength product.

For vodka, however, even this rectified spirit is not pure enough. It is then passed through beds of activated charcoal which remove all taste and smell, and leave a pure, neutral spirit which needs no maturation and may be bottled and consumed at once.

Flavoured Spirits

From early times spirits have been flavoured for a number of reasons, of which two are the most important:

> The medicinal properties of herbs were extracted by alcohol, and were easy to administer.

> Flavour from the herbs and spices disguised the often harsh taste of the spirit.

Today the most important flavoured spirit is gin.

Gin

There are two main styles of gin, **London dry** and **Dutch**. Most of the gin available in the UK is London dry.

There are three steps in the production of London dry gin:

1.   A low strength alcoholic wash, made from molasses or grain, is distilled in a patent still.

2.   This spirit is then re-distilled in a patent still to produce a highly rectified, neutral spirit.

3.   This rectified spirit is placed in a pot still with certain flavourings (which are known as 'botanicals'). It is then re-distilled and the flavours from these botanicals pass into the final spirit.

CORIANDERS   ANGELICA   JUNIPERS

Three of the main gin botanicals

Only the middle part of this final distillation is used.

Each distiller has his own secret recipe of botanicals, so all commercial gins made this way have a slightly different taste. The one botanical they all have in common is juniper berries. The name 'gin' is a corruption of the Dutch word for juniper, which is 'genever'.

The other major style of gin, Dutch gin, or genever, is made from a base of malted barley and rye, which is then distilled twice in a pot still, the second time with botanicals. It is a richer and heavier drink, usually drunk in small glasses, very cold and undiluted.

Other flavoured spirits

Aquavit from Scandinavia, whose main flavouring comes from caraway seeds.

Ouzo, the Greek spirit flavoured with aniseed.

Arrack, a crude spirit, drunk in Africa and the Middle and Far East. The distilled spirit is derived from the fermentation of various raw materials, including rice, palm sap, yams and dates.

Angostura bitters, which are made in Trinidad and based on rum.

Fernet branca, a bitters flavoured with herbs and orange peel.

The term **bitters** refers to spirits flavoured with barks, herbs and roots and which are always bitter on the palate. They may be employed as aperitifs or digestifs - that is, before or after the meal.

Liqueurs *sweetened & flavoured spirit*

A liqueur is a compounded spirit, which is made with clearly identifiable elements such as spirit, flavours, sweeteners and, often, colour.

All liqueurs contain three elements, and most contain a fourth.

Alcohol

Sugar syrup - It is important to remember that fruit spirits are not sweetened, but liqueurs are. For example, kirsch is unsweetened but cherry brandy is sweetened.

Flavourings - There are three ways of putting the flavour into a liqueur:

- The spirit may be distilled with the chosen flavouring in a pot still.
- The flavouring element may be in the alcohol for about four weeks. This method (maceration) is often used with soft fruits.
- The alcohol may be pumped over the flavouring in much the same way as water is pumped over coffee in a percolator (infusion).

Flavours are usually based on one of the following:

Herbs   - crème de menthe, green or yellow chartreuse, bénédictine.

Citrus fruit   - grand marnier, cointreau, curaçao

Stone fruit   - apricot, peach or cherry brandy

Kernels or Beans - creme de cacao (chocolate), Tia Maria (coffee)

Cream   - various branded cream liqueurs

Colour - Most liqueurs are coloured.

To complete the liqueur, all the ingredients are blended together and matured for a short period to allow them to marry.

Chapter 13
Low Strength Beverages

There are many people who like to enjoy the flavour of wine, beer or cider, without experiencing the effects of alcohol.

This applies not only to those who are teetotal. Some regular drinkers take this attitude on particular occasions, such as drivers who responsibly impose a limit on their alcohol consumption, or those who seek to moderate their overall intake.

There are now several products which attempt to satisfy this requirement. They resemble the desired beverage, but contain only small amounts of alcohol.

Production Methods

There are three approaches to the production of low strength beverages.

Short fermentation

Only a small amount of sugar is fermented to alcohol. This can be achieved either by fermenting a weak sugary solution to dryness, or by partially fermenting one of normal sweetness. In the first case a light flavour would result and in the latter case a residual sweetness.

Alcohol removal

A normal strength beer or wine is physically treated to separate the alcohol from the rest of the liquid.

One process involves heating to distil the alcohol. If gentle heat is applied to a depressurized container, the alcohol vaporises at a low temperature and so the flavour of the remaining liquid is not so seriously affected.

Another removal method employs a centrifuge to separate the component substances, so that the alcohol may be extracted.

Other techniques used are reverse osmosis and ultrafiltration, which allow separation of the alcohol from other flavouring substances in the product while retaining reasonable quality.

Blending

By mixing an alcoholic drink with non-alcoholic beverages such as fruit juice and mineral water, a blend results which is of low strength. These products are sometimes called 'coolers'.

Descriptions

Products with a lower than normal alcohol content may be variously described according to their alcohol content:

non-alcoholic	0%
alcohol free	less than 0.05%
dealcoholised	less than 0.5%
low alcohol	0.5% to 1.2%
reduced alcohol	1.2% to 5.5%

Note that products where the reduction in strength is due to dilution may not be described as 'reduced alcohol'.

Index

Notes

Notes

🏛 ISLINGTON

Please return this item on or before the last date stamped below or you may be liable to overdue charges. To renew an item call the number below, or access the online catalogue at www.islington.gov.uk/libraries. You will need your library membership number and PIN number.

12/10

TRANS AL 5.10.12	⁻ 3 SEP 2018	
1 6 NOV 2012		
1 2 JAN 2013		
2 4 MAR 2014		
1 7 AUG 2018		

For Lizzie Ryley

www.summerwaters.co.uk

First published in paperback by HarperCollins Children's Books in 20..

HarperCollins Children's Books is a division of HarperCollins Publishers Ltd,
77–85 Fulham Palace Road, Hammersmith, London W6 8JB.

Visit our website at: www.harpercollins.co.uk

2

ISBN: 978-0-00-736750-4

Typeset by Palimpsest Book Production Limited,
Falkirk, Stirlingshire

Printed and bound in England by Clays Ltd, S

Silver Dolphins

RIVER RESCUE

by **Summer Waters**

Silver Dolphins

RIVER RESCUE

HarperCollins *Children's Books*

Prologue

A group of dolphins were playing follow my leader along the seabed. In and out of the rocks they chased each other in a long, wiggly line.

"It's my turn to be leader now," clicked Swift, one of the older dolphins.

Swift swam fast, weaving between the rocks, turning somersaults and rolling in the water. The dolphins chased after him, squealing with delight.

"This is so much fun!" exclaimed Bubbles.

"Let's go and play in the kelp beds," said Swift. "That'll be even more fun."

"Bubbly," clicked Bubbles. "You lead and we'll follow."

But as Swift headed out to sea, a tiny dolphin named Dot called from the back, "Mum doesn't let me go to the kelp beds on my own."

"You're not on your own. You're with us," said Swift.

Dot stopped swimming and shook her head. "Sorry, but I'm not allowed to go there without a grown-up. Please can we play here?"

"I'm going to the kelp beds," said Swift firmly. "Stay here if you don't want to come."

"But I won't have anyone to play with," squeaked Dot.

"I'll stay behind with you," said Bubbles.

He darted out of the line and swam over to her.

"You said you'd go to the kelp beds," said Swift crossly. "You can't just change your mind."

"I can," said Bubbles.

"Well, I'm not changing mine," said Swift crossly. "Follow me, everyone."

The other dolphins hesitated, then some followed Swift and some stayed with Bubbles and Dot. They immediately started a new game, unaware that Spirit and Star were watching them.

"Bubbles was right," said Star proudly. "You *can* change your mind."

Spirit uttered a long sigh. "If only all choices were that simple. I sense much harder decisions ahead for the Silver Dolphins."

"Can we help them?" asked Star.

"No," said Spirit sadly. "The Silver Dolphins must choose for themselves."

Chapter One

ntonia Lee woke with the sun on her face and a wonderful feeling bubbling inside her. It was the first day of the spring holiday. Two whole weeks of fun and spending as much time as she liked helping at Sea Watch, the marine conservation charity run by her friend Cai's great-aunt Claudia. Hurriedly, Antonia

washed and dressed then went downstairs for breakfast.

Mum and Dad were drinking tea in the kitchen.

"You're up early," said Dad. "Did you forget there was no school?"

"I'm going to Sea Watch," said Antonia, pouring herself a bowl of cereal. "There's a lot to do because it's just volunteers today – Cai and Claudia aren't there this morning."

"Of course!" exclaimed Mum, passing Antonia a mug of tea. "They'll be on their way to the airport to collect Cai's parents."

Cai was living with his great-aunt Claudia in Sandy Bay because his mum and dad had temporary jobs in Australia.

"How long are they over here for?" asked Dad.

"Ten days," said Antonia. She finished her breakfast then sat on the kitchen floor to put on her trainers.

"Are you coming back for lunch?" Mum stepped over her to get to the dishwasher.

"No, I made some sandwiches last night. I'll be home for tea, though." Antonia's voice trailed away as a very familiar feeling swept over her. It made her tingle with anticipation. The dolphins needed her! Any minute now the silver dolphin charm Antonia always wore round her neck would call her to the sea.

"Got to go," she said, hurriedly jumping up. "See you later."

"Have a good day," called Mum.

As Antonia closed the front door her silver dolphin charm vibrated and its tiny tail tapped against her neck. The charm was as soft as a

real dolphin. Antonia shivered with delight as suddenly a high-pitched whistle that only a Silver Dolphin could hear shrilled from it.

Silver Dolphin, we need you.

Spirit, I hear your call, Antonia silently answered as she headed towards the beach.

Both Antonia and Cai were Silver Dolphins, or guardians of the sea. They had special magical abilities that let them swim and communicate with dolphins! With these amazing abilities came the responsibility to care for sea life. Antonia wished that Cai was there too as she ran towards Gull Bay. He'd be frustrated that he'd missed Spirit's call, even though he was really excited about meeting his parents at the airport. Antonia jumped down on to the deserted beach. The soft, white sand shifted beneath her feet as

she ran over to the rocks. Pulling off her trainers and socks, Antonia left them under a rock and ran down to the sea. The water was chilly and her teeth chattered as she waded deeper. There were goose bumps on her arms and legs, but Antonia kept walking. When the sea was deep enough she gracefully dived in. The water was so cold it made her gasp, but she quickly warmed up as her legs melded together to kick like a dolphin's tail. Hands paddling like flippers, body arching in and out of the sea, Antonia swam to find Spirit.

It wasn't long before she saw four silver heads in the water. Antonia swam on, pleased that Spirit had brought his family – Star, Dream and Bubbles – with him. She greeted Spirit first, rubbing her nose against his. Bubbles impatiently bobbed in the water, waiting for

his turn, then greeted Antonia enthusiastically.

"Thank you for answering our call, Silver Dolphin," said Spirit. "Bubbles and Dream have found an old fishing net on the seabed."

"Show me where," said Antonia at once. Lost or abandoned fishing nets posed a serious threat to sea life. If animals got stuck in them they either starved or drowned.

"Follow me," said Bubbles importantly.

Antonia dived under the sea and swam after Bubbles, with Spirit, Star and Dream following.

"There," said Bubbles, pointing with his nose.

"Don't get too close," Spirit clicked in warning as Bubbles swam nearer.

The net was like a hideous brown monster slumbering on the seabed. Antonia swam round it, her eyes quickly sliding over the rotting fish and the dead starfish trapped in

its squares. It was large and would be awkward to carry, but she thought she could manage it on her own. Fighting back her revulsion, Antonia pulled the dead creatures away then carefully folded the net in half and rolled it into a bundle.

"Stay back," she warned as Bubbles inched closer to see what she was doing.

Antonia scooped the net up and swam upwards until her head broke through the water's surface.

"Phew," she panted. "It's heavy."

"When he arrives the other Silver Dolphin will help you get it ashore," said Bubbles confidently.

"He's not coming," said Antonia. "He's gone to meet his parents. They've come back from Australia to visit him."

"That's lovely. He must really miss them," clicked Star sympathetically.

"He does," said Antonia.

Bubbles looked scared. "What if he decides to go and live in Australia with his parents?" he asked.

Antonia laughed and said confidently, "That won't happen. Cai loves it here. Being a Silver Dolphin is the best thing that's ever happened to him."

The net was weighing her down so she headed to shore. The dolphins swam with her, clicking encouragement but not offering any help – nets were too dangerous. Soon Antonia was red in the face with exertion.

"Not far now," she panted as the beach drew closer.

"Can the Silver Dolphin come back and play

when she's taken the net ashore?" asked Bubbles hopefully.

"Yes, if she'd like to," clicked Spirit.

Antonia shook her head sadly. "I'd love to, but I can't. I'm needed at Sea Watch today. I'll play another time."

Bubbles looked disappointed as he said goodbye, splashing his tail in the water.

Antonia headed straight for the beach. When it was shallow enough to paddle, she dumped the net in the surf while she caught her breath. Sea water poured from her clothes like a miniature waterfall, leaving everything as dry as if she'd never been in the water. Antonia ran her hand through her long, blonde hair, straightening out a few damp tangles. A nasty odour was coming from the net. Antonia wrinkled her nose and, holding it carefully

away from her, carried it up the beach and fed it into the dustbin. If Cai had been there to help she would have taken the net back to the Sea Watch bin rather than fill the one on the beach, but it was too heavy and smelly to carry to Sea Watch on her own.

Antonia put on her shoes and socks, chuckling as she remembered Bubbles's comment about Cai returning to live with his parents. Cai was very excited about seeing his mum and dad, but there was no way he'd go back to Australia with them. His world was here in Sandy Bay. Thinking about the fun times they'd had together, Antonia hurried to Sea Watch.

Chapter Two

It felt funny going to Sea Watch, knowing that neither Cai or Claudia would be there. The door was unlocked, but the building had an empty feel to it.

"Hello, is anyone here?" called Antonia.

"Hi, Antonia, I'm in the back room," Sally, an adult volunteer who took charge when Claudia was away, called out.

Antonia opened the door and found Sally sitting on a chair, feeding a fox cub with a baby's bottle.

"You're early," Sally said, smiling at Antonia.

"Not as early as you," said Antonia, smiling back. "Oh, how sweet! When did the fox cub come in?"

"This is Rusty. A motorist brought him in last night. His mother was killed by a car. The motorist found him lying next to her at the side of the road."

Antonia stood very still, watching the cub suck lethargically from the bottle of milk. He had chocolate-coloured fur, large ears and a tiny black nose.

"He's so cute," she whispered.

Rusty couldn't finish the bottle. Sally